MATHEMATICS

Uniform with this volume
and in the same series

TEACH YOURSELF

MATHEMATICS

A BOOK OF SELF-INSTRUCTION IN
ESSENTIAL MATHEMATICS BASED ON
THE WORK BY JOHN DAVIDSON, M.A.

THE ENGLISH UNIVERSITIES PRESS LTD

ST PAUL'S HOUSE   WARWICK LANE
LONDON EC4

First printed 1938
New edition 1965
This impression 1968

SBN   340   05648   7

Printed in Great Britain for The English Universities Press, Ltd.,
by Richard Clay (The Chaucer Press), Ltd., Bungay Suffolk

CONTENTS

1.	Explanation of Some Common Terms and Signs Used in Mathematics	9
2.	Introduction to Algebra	19
3.	Multiplication and Division in Algebra	30
4.	Factors and Multiples—Highest Common Factor—Lowest Common Multiple	37
5.	Methods of Shortening Multiplication and Division	42
6.	The Use of Brackets	49
7.	Evaluating Algebraic Expressions	52
8.	Fractions	55
9.	Simple Algebraic Fractions	64
10.	Decimals	66
11.	Calculations with Decimals and Fractions	74
12.	Weights and Measures	81
13.	Squares, Cubes, Square and Cube Roots	92
14.	Simple Equations and Problems	100
15.	Simultaneous Equations	110
16.	Ratio—Proportion—Unitary Method	116
17.	Proportional Parts	131
18.	Averages	137
19.	Percentages	140
20.	Areas of Rectangular Figures	147
21.	Volumes of Rectangular Solids	156
22.	Areas and Volumes of Common Figures	160
23.	Business Mathematics	167
	Answers	181

INTRODUCTION

THIS volume is intended to help the isolated student to master the elementary principles of Mathematics, and to apply them to the purely practical calculations of ordinary life. There is no attempt whatsoever to emulate the many excellent text-books on Arithmetic that are now available. But to many students the ordinary text-book, with its rigorous scientific treatment of the subject, too often acts as a formidable deterrent to study. For such students this book is designed. It does not promise them a royal road towards becoming expert and skilful calculators; but it tries to smooth the way for him who is not averse to a little thinking. It does this, in the first place, by avoiding as much as possible rigorously scientific explanations, and adopting a more or less free manner of treatment. Secondly, just so much of the theory of the various rules is given as is absolutely necessary to a practical understanding of the rules. One who calculates purely by "rule of thumb" and without an understanding of the reason of his processes is perfectly unable to use his instrument except in one particular groove. Thirdly, the exercises for practice given in connection with the various rules are for the most part of a thoroughly practical nature. Except here and there, for the sake of a little thinking exercise, all such fancy problems as those connected with our old friends the hounds and hares, the hands of a clock, the climbing snail, are studiously avoided. These are excellent material for mental gymnastics; but they are luxuries, and are out of place in a

book which is meant to supply only the arithmetical
necessities of life. Fourthly, under each rule worked-out
examples are given of the most typical calculations that
come under the rule. In many cases an example is
worked out in several ways, for the purpose of contrasting
long and short methods and of encouraging the student
to keep his eyes open for the latter methods, which, *from
a practical point of view*, must be the best methods. As
to getting confused by a display of several methods, the
student who is willing to think a little need have no fear.
If he really masters fractions and fractional methods, a
little practice will soon enable him to detect unerringly—

(1) the particular rule by which a calculation can
best be performed; and
(2) the shortest way of working *under* that rule.

A suggestion as to method of working. Every student
who feels himself weak in fractional work ought to read
and master thoroughly the chapters on fractions and
work through the various set exercises. The answers to
these exercises find their proper place at the end of the
book, where they are to be consulted as a corroboration
of the reader's own calculations when these have been
performed *absolutely without knowledge of the given answer*.
He who works with the answer in his pocket, as it were,
will never be sure of himself.

This distrust of oneself in arithmetical work is apt to be
more pronounced when answers will not come out neatly.
In the exercises of this book very many of the answers are
of this "nasty" character. But they are no worse than
the actual results we have to encounter in daily life. And
it is well that the practical student should get accustomed
to problems that are not engineered to secure neat
answers; and so to perfect his calculating power as to be
able to trust himself in the case of "nasty" answers.

Here and there throughout the book hints are given as to how awkward results are treated in practical work.

After the study of fractions, it does not much matter which rule the student then takes up, although it is as well for the general student to follow the order in which they are hereafter treated. The student who consults this book for guidance in a particular brand of calculation will of course find his practical needs determining his choice. Such a student, however, is advised to look at other rules than those under which his own particular problems mainly come; for the rules throw light on one another; and in not a few cases a problem that at first sight apparently ranks under a certain rule is found to be much more easily solved by some other rule.

CHAPTER ONE

EXPLANATION OF SOME COMMON TERMS AND SIGNS USED IN MATHEMATICS

In mathematics, as in every other subject of study, certain special words or terms are used to represent ideas and operations that occur over and over again. Now, these ideas and operations in mathematics are very closely related to one another. Thus, the idea of a *divisor* involves the idea of three things: (1) something *to be divided*; (2) something to *divide it*; and (3) the *result* of the dividing operation.

Now, if the student does not understand (1) the exact meanings of these ever-recurring words, and (2) the exact relationship between the *things* for which the words stand, he cannot properly understand mathematical explanations in which these words must be used, nor can he be thoroughly sure of his own mathematical calculations.

The student is therefore urged, before passing on further, to see that he has a perfectly clear idea of what we shall here put in as short a form as possible.

A unit or a unit quantity (from the Latin word *unus*, one) is the name given to a quantity when we use it for the purpose of comparing the magnitudes of other quantities of the *same kind as itself*. Thus, in speaking of a sum of money as £5 or £12, we are using the unit "pound sterling" for the purpose of comparing the sum with the unit. Again, in speaking of a distance as 10 miles, we are using the unit "mile" for the purpose of comparing the distance with the unit. The unit really serves as a *standard of comparison*. Without some

standard of comparison we could not calculate at all,
and without a standard that is the *same* for all of us we
could not understand each other's calculations. Note
that the unit is not necessarily one single thing. Thus,
suppose we have 10 *groups* of marbles, and that each
group contains 10 *marbles*, then "1 group" is the unit in
relation to the 10 *groups*, but "1 marble" is the unit in
relation to "1 group". Thus, in our method of numbering,
we write 234 for two hundred and thirty-four; here 1 is
the unit in relation to the 4, a *group* of ten is the unit in
relation to the 3 and a *group* of a hundred is the unit in
relation to the 2.

Addition

Addition is the process of finding the sum of two or
more given numbers. The sign + (read "plus", from
Latin *plus*, meaning "more") is often used to indicate
the addition of numbers. Thus, $5 + 7$ means the sum of
5 and 7, and is read "5 plus 7".

If we wish to indicate that $5 + 7$ equals 12 we use the
sign =, which is read "is equal to" or "equals". This is
a very convenient sign, and will be very frequently used
throughout the book to express the equality between
numbers.

We can use the symbol + repeatedly between any
numbers to be added.

e.g., $18 + 3 + 8 + 12 = 41$

Example 1. $113 + 27 + 58$.

We first add the units: $3 + 7 + 8 = 18$; put 8 down
as the unit in our answer and carry 1 ten. Now add the
tens: $1 + 2 + 5 = 8$, add the 1 ten carried to make 9.
Put down the 9 as our tens in the answer. Add the
hundreds, $1 + 0 + 0 = 1$. Put down the 1 as our
hundreds in the answer.

Therefore $113 + 27 + 58 = 198$.

Example 2. Add 68, 1 351 and 621.

To simplify addition we can list our numbers to be added in a column, placing the units in one column, the tens in another, etc.

This gives
$$\begin{array}{r} 68 \\ 1\,351 \\ 621 \\ \hline \\ \hline \end{array}$$

Add the units: $8 + 1 + 1 = 10$; put down 0, carry 1 ten.

Add the tens: $6 + 5 + 2 = 13$; add the 1 carried over from the units to give 14. Put down 4, carry 1.

Add the hundreds: $0 + 3 + 6 = 9$; add the 1 carried over from the tens to give 10. Put down 0, carry 1.

Add the thousands: $0 + 1 + 0 = 1$; add the 1 carried over from the hundreds to give 2. Put down 2.

Note. The above calculations should be done in the reader's head, so that the problem would be written thus:

$$\begin{array}{r} 68 \\ 1\,351 \\ 621 \\ \hline 2\,040 \\ \hline 1\ 1\ 1 \end{array}$$

Subtraction

Subtraction is the process of finding the *difference* between two given numbers. The sign — (read "minus", from Latin *minus*, less) is often used to indicate subtraction. Thus, $10 - 7$ means that 7 is to be subtracted from 10, and is read "10 minus 7". Using the sign of equality we may write $10 - 7 = 3$.

Example 3. Subtract 235 from 416.

Subtract the units: $6 - 5 = 1$; put down 1.

Subtract the tens: We cannot subtract 3 from 1, so borrow 1 hundred from the hundreds column and read: $11 - 3$. This gives 8, which we put down as our tens in the answer.

Subtract the hundreds: Add the 1 we borrowed back to the hundred figure in 235 (i.e., $2 + 1 = 3$). We then subtract 3 from 4 to give 1, which we put down in our answer.

Thus $416 - 235 = 181$.

Example 4. In a college there are 1 327 students. If there are 837 men, how many women are there?

This can be written as follows:

$$
\begin{array}{r}
{\scriptstyle 1\,1} \\
1\,327\ - \\
{}^{9}837 \\
\hline
490 \\
\hline
\end{array}
$$

Thus there are 490 women in the college.

Note. The calculation is done in a similar way to Example 3. When we "borrow" or "add back" we show this on the sum as shown.

Quick Methods in Addition and Subtraction

1. *Addition*. Add 593 to 725.

The method which gives the easiest solution to this problem is to add 600 to 725 and then subtract 7. This gives 1 318.

Note. To add 488—add 500 and subtract 12.

To add 395—add 400 and subtract 5.

2. *Subtraction.* Subtract 592 from 915.

The method which gives us a quick answer to this problem is to subtract 600 from 915 and then add 8. This gives 323.

Note. To subtract 197—subtract 200 and add 3.

To subtract 889—subtract 900 and add 11.

Brackets in Addition and Subtraction

We can sometimes shorten our statements by the use of brackets. Thus, if we wish to indicate that 5 and 7 are first to be added and then subtracted from 18, we can show this by means of brackets:

therefore $18 - (5 + 7) = 6$, since $5 + 7 = 12$, and $18 - 12 = 6$.

A second example is obtained by considering:

$$(5 + 7) - \{5 - (2 + 1)\}.$$

This means that 2 and 1 are to be first added, then subtracted from 5, and the result subtracted from the sum of 5 and 7. A fuller explanation of the use of brackets will be found in Chapter Six.

Enough has been said here about brackets to enable the student to understand all the ordinary mathematical processes.

Multiplication

Multiplication is a convenient process of finding the *sum* of a given number of repetitions of a certain number. Thus, the *sum* of 5 repetitions of $25 = 25 + 25 + 25 +$

25 + 25, that is, 25 taken 5 times, or 25 multiplied by 5, which is equal to 125.

Note that 5 and 25 are called *factors* of 125

Example 5. If six rows of trees are laid out in an orchard with 8 trees in each row, we could add the number of trees either as

(i) 6 lots of 8: $8 + 8 + 8 + 8 + 8 + 8 = 48$

or

(ii) 8 lots of 6: $6 + 6 + 6 + 6 + 6 + 6 + 6 + 6 = 48$.

This working is greatly reduced by writing (i) as $6 \times 8 = 48$ and (ii) as $8 \times 6 = 48$. These read as six times eight equals 48 and eight times six equals 48. The symbol $\times$ therefore means "times" or "multiplied by".

Example 6. Multiply 342 by 11.

This is written as

$$342 \times$$
$$11$$
$$\overline{}$$
$$\overline{}$$

As this problem contains numbers which make it difficult to calculate the answer in our heads, we find our solution by first considering the "unit" answer, second the "ten" answers, etc.

We, therefore, solve the problem as follows:

$2 \times 11 = 22$, put down 2 as our unit and carry 2
$4 \times 11 = 44$, (add 2 from units $= 46$) put down 6 and carry 4
$3 \times 11 = 33$, (add 4 $= 37$) put down 37.

Therefore $342 \times 11 = 3\,762$.

Note. If we do not wish to write down each step in the solution, this problem is written as follows:

$$
\begin{array}{r}
342 \times \\
11 \\
\hline
3\,762 \\
\hline
4\,2
\end{array}
$$

Division

Division is the process of sharing or finding how many *times* a given number is found in another given number. Of course, we could find this out by subtracting the smaller number from the larger number, then subtracting it again from the remainder, and so on till there was no remainder. Then the number of times required would be the number of times we subtracted the smaller number. The process of division enables us to perform this subtraction more rapidly. And it does this by the aid of multiplication. Thus, in the division of 8 by 2, we know that 2 taken 4 times, that is 2×4, $= 8$; and so we say that 2 can be taken from 8 four times, or that 2 is contained in 8 four times.

Example 7. Divide 156 by 12.

$156 \div 12 = 13$ (because 13 lots of 12 made 156)

Example 8. Divide 3 681 by 3.

We write this as:

$$3)\overline{3681}$$

First we consider our thousand column in the dividend (note that we always consider the largest column first in division, which means that we perform our calculation by working from left to right). Therefore 3 into 3 divides

1, which we place in our answer column. 3 into 6 divides 2, which we put down. 3 into 8 divides 2, which we put down and carry 2 tens to our unit column. This gives 20 + 1 = 21. 3 into 21 gives 7, which completes our answer.

This is written

$$3) \overset{2}{3\ 68\overset{2}{1}}$$
$$\overline{1\ 227}$$

This is called *short division*.

Example 9. Divide 213 by 39.

$$\begin{array}{r} 55 \\ \hline 39)2\ 145 \\ 1\ 95 \\ \hline 195 \\ 195 \\ \hline \cdots \\ \hline \end{array}$$

This calculation is performed by the same processes as used in Example 8, but since we are dealing with larger numbers, we do our calculations (subtractions) below the dividend. This is *long division*, and is usually used when the divisor is larger than 12.

Squares

The *square* of a given number is the product of *two* factors, each equal to the number. Thus, 25 is the square of 5; 36 is the square of 6; 100 is the square of 10; and so on.

To indicate that a number is to be *squared*, we put the

figure 2 at the upper right-hand corner of the number; thus, 5^2 means 5×5, or 5 squared, that is 25.

Cubes

Similarly, 5^3 means $5 \times 5 \times 5$, or 5 *cubed*, that is 125; 10^3 means $10 \times 10 \times 10$, that is 1 000; and so on.

Square Roots

The *square root* of a given number is that number which, when multiplied by itself once, gives as a result the given number. Thus, 5 is the square root of 25; 6 is the square root of 36; 10 is the square root of 100; and so on. When we find the square root of a number we say we are *extracting the square root*.

The sign $\sqrt{\ }$ (which is really a modified form of the letter "r", the first letter of the word "root") is used to indicate the square root. Thus $\sqrt{25}$ means "the square root of 25", that is 5.

Cube Roots

If we wish to indicate that we want to find the *cube root* of a given number, we use the sign $\sqrt[3]{\ }$, and so with regard to other roots—$\sqrt[4]{\ }$, $\sqrt[5]{\ }$, etc.

Thus (1) $\sqrt[3]{125}$ means the cube root of 125, which is 5; for $5 \times 5 \times 5 = 125$; (2) $\sqrt[3]{1\,000} = 10$; for $10 \times 10 \times 10 = 1\,000$.

EXERCISE 1

1. Add together: (a) $18 + 5 + 6$; (b) $31 + 64 + 81$; (c) $21 + 11 + 39$.

2. Add: (a) 35   (b) 341   (c) 653
             17   238   475
             21   1 021   318

3. Subtract: (a) 38 from 121;   (b) 64 from 192;
             (c) 141 from 738.

4. Find the value of: (a) $38 + 72 - 41$; (b) $56 + 128 - 98$;
             (c) $348 + 836 - 947$.

5. Multiply: (*a*) 38 by 11;   (*b*) 35 by 21;   (*c*) 438 by 27.
6. Divide: (*a*) 836 by 11;   (*b*) 3 934 by 14;
                   (*c*) 2 072 by 37.
7. Solve 832 + 727 − 649.
8. Solve 38 × 9 × 7 ÷ 3 ÷ 2.
9. Find the *squares* of 2, 3, 4, 5, 6, 7, 8, 9, 10, 11, 12, 13, 14, 15, 16, 17, 18, 19, 20.
10. Find the *square root* of each of the following numbers: 25, 4, 16, 81, 144; 225, 9, 49, 100, 169; 361, 196, 289, 1, 121; 400, 324, 36, 64.

CHAPTER TWO

INTRODUCTION TO ALGEBRA

IN chapter one we have been dealing with *definite numbers* in all our arithmetical calculations. Algebra deals also with definite numbers, but more often introduces *general expressions* which give us *general results* to problems.

We shall show this difference by discussing a number of problems.

Let us consider a team of fifteen footballers whose total weight is 2 730 pounds. To find the average weight of the footballers we must divide their total weight by the number in the team. Thus, as explained in the section on division in Chapter One, we obtain the average weight, which is 182 pounds. This solution has been obtained by an arithmetical calculation which has dealt with definite numbers.

By using algebra we can obtain a *general expression* which will give a *general result* to the above problem. Now if we let x represent the number of footballers, y represent their total weight and z their average weight we obtain the general expression

$$z = \frac{y}{x}$$

This is an *algebraic expression* which says that the average weight of a footballer in a team (z) is equal to the total weight of the team (y) divided by the number of footballers (x). The reader will see that this general expression is true if we substitute the values used in our arithmetical problems.

The meaning and utility of elementary Algebra may be made clear by the following:

If a body is set in motion the only reason why it should come to a stop is because it is acted upon by some force. For example, a ball set rolling along the ground only stops because the friction of the ground and of the air gradually stops it. Now, it has been proved that there is a fixed relation between the mass of the moving body, the force, and the time during which the body is changing from one velocity to another. If the force be represented by F, the mass by m, the time by t, the first velocity by v_1, and the second velocity by v, then $F \times t = m \times (v_1 - v)$, or in words, the force multiplied by the time = the product of the mass by the difference of the velocities.

The above form will be true whatever values F, t, m, v and v_1 may have. The moment we attach arithmetical numbers to the letters the result is true *only of those numbers*. But *as it stands* it is true of all problems involving force, time, mass and velocity. It is applicable to all; it is *general*, not particular. And it is *general* because the letters, unlike numbers 1, 4, 6, etc., stand for *any numbers whatsoever*. The form we call *algebraical*, as opposed to *arithmetical*. And it is evident that the form, or *formula*, as it is called, is a very convenient method of remembering scientific laws upon which so many practical problems depend. Thus all the experiments connected with projectiles depend upon the above and similar formulae. But there are other numerous relationships among natural objects that it is useful and necessary for many people to know, and which are conveniently expressed in *formulae*. Further, many an arithmetical problem can be more readily solved by algebraical methods than by arithmetical. The working out of these formulae, according to the various given values of the letters, must depend, as all calculation does, on the four fundamental operations of addition, subtraction, multiplication and division. Only, as *letters* are employed, as well as arithmetical numbers, to represent quantities, it may be expected that there will be some differences between arithmetical and algebraical operations. These differences, however, are more apparent than real; and if the student makes up his mind to see in algebraical operations only arithmetical processes *generalised*, he ought to find little difficulty in mastering sufficient algebra to serve ordinary practical purposes.

Explanation of Symbols

1. In Arithmetic 2, 5, 8, 10, etc., are definite numbers, that is, each has a *fixed* value.

In Algebra a, b, c, d, x, y, z, stand for *any values*.

In the same expression, however, such as $a + b - c + 2a - 3b$, the same letter is supposed to have the same value wherever it occurs.

Note. The letters a, b, c, etc., and the signs $+$, $-$, $\times$, etc., are called algebraic symbols, and any collection of algebraic symbols is called an *algebraic expression*. Thus $a + b - c$, $x - y + \sqrt{z}$, etc., are algebraic expressions.

The parts of an algebraic expression which are separated by the signs $+$ and $-$ are called the *terms* of the expression. Thus a, $+ b$, $- c$, are the terms of the first expression above, and x, $- y$, $+ \sqrt{z}$, are the terms of the second.

2. In Arithmetic and Algebra the sign $+$ has the same meaning, viz., to denote addition. Thus, in Arithmetic, $2 + 4 = 6$; in Algebra $a + b$ means the sum of the quantities a and b.

In Arithmetic the sign $-$ always means that the quantity which follows it is *less* than the quantity preceding it, and is to be extracted from it.

In Algebra the sign $-$ is often used to denote that a

larger quantity is subtracted from a less. Now this can only be by employing the notion of a quantity *less* than o, that is, a *negative quantity*. But this notion after all is not difficult to realise. Suppose that A possesses £100 and that B, instead of possessing any money at all, is in debt to the extent of £100. B's *wealth* cannot be represented by £o, but by − £100.

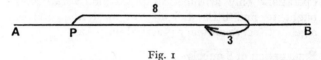

Fig. 1

Again, suppose that a man starts from a certain milestone to walk along a road. Let AB in Fig. 1 represent the road, P the starting-point and PB the direction in which the man walks. If he walks 8 miles in the direction PB, then turns and walks 3 miles back in the opposite direction, he will at the end of his walk be 8 − 3 or 5

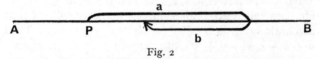

Fig. 2

miles from P, this distance being measured in the direction PB. Denote this by + 5. In general, if he walks a miles in the direction PB and b miles back (see Fig. 2), he will finally be $a − b$ miles from P.

Suppose now that we take $a = 8$ and $b = 12$, then $a − b = 8 − 12 = − 4$ (see Fig. 3). What, then, does this result mean? Can we give a meaning to it? Well, we know that if the man walks 8 miles in the direction PB

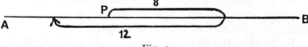

Fig. 3

and 12 miles back in the opposite direction, he will be 4 miles on the opposite side of P. Hence -4 is interpreted as meaning 4 measured in a direction *opposite* to PB. In other words, if $+4$ denotes a distance of 4 miles measured from P in the direction PB, -4 denotes a distance of 4 miles measured from P in the opposite direction.

It is clear that we may choose either direction as the positive or $+$ direction. Thus, if we take PA to be the positive direction, PB will be the negative $(-)$ direction; and $+4$ will denote a distance measured in the direction PA, while -4 will denote a distance measured in the direction PB.

Again, take the measurement on the Centigrade (or Celsius) thermometer. On that thermometer the temperature at which water freezes is marked $0°$ (no degrees), and that at which water boils is marked $100°$ (100 degrees). But there are *lower* temperatures than $0°$ to which it is often necessary to refer, and these must be marked $-$. Thus $+3°$ C. or $3°$ C. indicates 3 degrees *above* freezing-point, and $-3°$ C. indicates 3 degrees *below* freezing-point.

Hence:

3. A *sum*, or an addition, in Algebra may be the addition of *both positive and negative quantities*. For example, the sum of $+a$ and $-b$ is represented by the expression $+a-b$, or simply $a-b$. Then if $a=3$ and $b=5$, $a-b$ would mean $+3-5$, or -2, or the *sum* of a positive 3 and a negative 5 is a negative 2.

4. In arithmetic 53 is a short way of representing $50+3$, that is, $5 \times 10 + 3$, the 5 on account of its position representing not 5 units but 5 *tens*, that is, 5×10 units.

In Algebra such an expression as ab does not mean $10a+b$. The expressions ab, cd, xy, $3xy$, $6c$ all represent products. Thus $ab = a \times b$, $3xy = 3 \times x \times y$; a and b are the factors of ab, and 3, x, y are the factors of $3xy$.

In the product $3xy$, 3 is called the *numerical coefficient* of xy, x and y the *literal* (or letter) coefficients of 3. If the quantities are complex, their product is expressed by using *brackets*. For example, the product of $a + b$ and $c + d$ may be expressed as $(a + b) \times (c + d)$, or, more usually $(a + b)(c + d)$.

5. If the same quantity is multiplied by itself several times the product is expressed by writing the number of factors at the top right-hand corner of the quantity. Thus, the product $a \times a \times a \times a$ contains the factor a four times, and is therefore expressed as a^4—called a to the fourth *power*. Similarly, $x \times x \times x \times x \times x = x^5$, or x to the fifth *power* and $2 \times 2 \times 2 \times 2 \times 2 \times 2 = 2^6$, or 2 to the sixth *power*.

The number expressing the power of any quantity is called its *index* or *exponent*. Thus, in a^2, 2^3, x^7, the little figures 2, 3, 7 are the *indices* of a^2, 2^3, x^7 respectively. When the index is unity we do not write a^1 but simply a.

Note. Distinguish between a *coefficient* and an *index*. Thus, there is a difference between $6a$ and a^6:

$$6a = a + a + a + a + a + a.$$
$$a^6 = a \times a \times a \times a \times a \times a.$$

Addition in Algebra

Like Terms

Example 1. Find the sum of $6x$, $3x$, $-10x$, $-3x$, $5x$, $-2x$. Here the positive $(+)$ terms amount to $14x$ $(6x + 3x + 5x)$; the negative (-1) terms amount to $15x$ $(10x + 3x + 2x)$. Thus the sum of the positive and negative terms is $+14x - 15x = -x$. Hence **the rule of addition**: Add all the positive terms, add all the negative terms, and find the difference between the two sums. This difference has the sign of the *greater* sum.

Unlike Terms

Just as in arithmetic we cannot add different units except by keeping like quantities in the same column and unlike quantities in different columns, so in algebraical addition we place like terms in the same column, unlike terms in different columns. The necessity for this may be made quite evident from the following. The sum of £5 and 5s. is neither £10 nor 10s., but simply £5 5s.; so the sum of $2a$ and $2b$ is neither $4a$ nor $4b$, but simply $2a + 2b$.

Example 2. To find the sum of the quantities $2a$, $- b$, c, $- d$, $6a$, $3b$, $- 2a$, $- 3d$, we arrange the quantities as follows:

$$
\begin{array}{l}
2a - b + c - d \\
6a + 3b \\
- 2a \qquad\qquad - 3d \\
\hline
\end{array}
$$

Then, sum $=\quad 6a + 2b + c - 4d$

Example 3. To find the sum of the quantities x^2, $- 7x^2$, $9ab$, $4bc$, $- 3x^2$, $6bc$, $- 2ab$, $- xy$. The quantities are arranged as follows:

$$
\begin{array}{l}
x^2 + 9ab + 4bc \\
- 7x^2 - 2ab + 6bc \\
- 3x^2 \qquad\qquad - xy \\
\hline
\end{array}
$$

Then, sum $=- 9x^2 + 7ab + 10bc - xy$

Sometimes the expressions to be added consist of more than single terms, but the process of adding is the same as before.

Example 4. To find the sum of $a + 2b - c$, $6a - b$, $- a - b$, $7a - b$, $3a - b + c$, $5a + b - 2c$.

The arrangement is as follows:

$$a + 2b - c$$
$$6a - b$$
$$-a - b$$
$$7a - b$$
$$3a - b + c$$
$$5a + b - 2c$$

Then, sum $= 21a - b - 2c$

EXERCISE 2

Add together:

1. $a, -5a, -7a, 6a, 10a, -3a$.
2. $4b, -10b, 6b, -3b, -14b$.
3. $x, -2x, 5x, 7x, -8x, -9x$.
4. $2d, -3d, -4d, 6d, -7d$.
5. $x^2, 4x^2, -x^2, -9x^2, -7x^2$.
6. $xy, -6xy, 5xy, -2xy, -7xy$.
7. $x^2y, -7x^2y, -2x^2y, -8x^2y, 9x^2y$.
8. $2a - b - c, 3a - 2b - c + d, 7a - 2b, 9c$.
9. $8xy - 2b + y, 9b - y, 2xy + b + y, 4xy - y - 3b$.
10. $a^2 - 2ab + b^2, 3a^2 - ab - b^2, 6ab + b^2, 9a^2 - b^2$.
11. (a) $cx + cy - yz, \qquad 7cx - 2cy + 3yz, \qquad -8cx + 2cy,$
    $-3cx - 2cy - yz$.
    (b) Find the value of the result when $c = 1, x = 2, y = 3,$
    $z = 4$.
12. (a) $ax - 2bx - 6cx, \quad 3ax - cx, \quad 3bx + cx, \quad -5ax + bx,$
    $2ax - bx - cx$.
    (b) Find the value of the result when $a = 2, b = 1, c = 3,$
    $x = 7$.
13. $\frac{3}{4}x + \frac{1}{3}xy - \frac{1}{6}y, \frac{1}{2}x - 2xy, -\frac{1}{3}y - \frac{1}{4}x, 3x - \frac{1}{4}xy$.
14. $\frac{1}{2}a^3 - 2a^2b + \frac{3}{2}b^3, -\frac{1}{4}a^3 - a^2b, -a^2b - \frac{1}{2}b^3$.
15. $-2a - \frac{5}{2}c, 6a + \frac{3}{2}c, 5a - 2c, -6a - \frac{1}{3}c, 9a + c$.

Subtraction in Algebra

The following explanation may help you to understand the reason for the algebraic rule of subtraction.

Consider the following expressions:

(1) $a + (b - c)$.   (2) $a - (b - c)$.

The first means that *a* is to be added to the difference of *b* and *c*, and this is the same thing as first to add *b* to *a* and then subtract *c*. Hence $a + (b - c) = a + b - c$. That is, when $+$ precedes the bracket, the removal of the bracket does not affect the signs of the quantities inside the bracket.

Another way of looking at the expression is to think of the $+$ as adding to *a* every quantity within the brackets.

The second expression, $a - (b - c)$, means that $b - c$ is to be subtracted from *a*, or that *every quantity within the brackets is to be subtracted from a*. Now, the subtraction of *b* from *a* is represented by the expression $a - b$. What of the subtraction of $-c$ from *a*, that is, the subtraction of a *negative* quantity?

Fig. 4 shows the effect of a minus sign on a negative quantity.

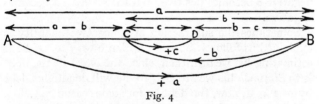

Fig. 4

Let AB be represented by *a*, and let the positive direction be from A to B (marked by the arrow). Suppose the length CB represents *b*, and CD represents *c*. Then $b - c$ is clearly the length represented by DB, so that $a - (b - c)$ is the length represented by AD. It is also clear, however, that AC represents $a - b$, so that AD also represents $(a - b) + c$, i.e., $a - b + c$. Therefore $a - (b - c) = a - b + c$, since these expressions are both represented by AD. Hence the rule: If a minus sign precedes a bracketed expression, on the removal of the brackets each $+$ becomes $-$, and each

— becomes $+$; or in other words, to subtract one quantity from another *change all the signs of the terms to be subtracted*.

Fig. 5 further illustrates the truth of the rule that

$$a - (b - c + d) = a - b + c - d,$$

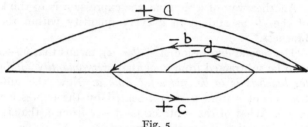

Fig. 5

where the positive quantity b becomes negative, the negative c becomes positive, and the positive d becomes negative.

Sometimes the subtraction of a negative quantity is explained as follows: Suppose a man owes £10. If he is estimating his wealth, then, since the effect of the debt is to *diminish* his wealth by £10, he will denote his debt by $- 10$. If, now, the debt be for some reason cancelled or taken away, that is, *subtracted*, the man will be richer by £10; and the result will be the same as if £10 had been added to his wealth; so that to *subtract* $- 10$ is the same as to add $+ 10$. Thus, $+ 20 - (- 10) = 20 + 10$.

Example 5. From $3a - 2b + c - 3d + e$ take $- 2a + 6b - c - 2d - 5e$.

First method:

$$3a - 2b + c - 3d + e - (- 2a + 6b - c - 2d - 5e)$$
$$= 3a - 2b + c - 3d + e + 2a - 6b + c + 2d + 5e$$
$$= 5a - 8b + 2c - d + 6e.$$

A second and more convenient method is to arrange the second expression under the first as in arithmetic, *to think of the signs as changed*, and then add, thus:

$$3a - 2b + c - 3d + e$$
$$- 2a + 6b - c - 2d - 5e$$

$$5a - 8b + 2c - d + 6e$$

Example 6.

From $5ax - 2by + 7xy - z$
Take $9ax + by - 3xy - 2z$

$$- 4ax - 3by + 10xy + z$$

Exercise 3

Subtract:

    1. $3a - b + c$ from $-6a - b$.
    2. $9x - y + z$ from $-3x + 2y - 2z$.
    3. $8ab - 2xy$ from $-ab - xy + z$.
    4. $x^2 - y^2$ from $-x^2 - y^2$.
    5. $7xy + 2yz - 3xz$ from $-xy - xz$.

From:

    6. $-p - q + r$ take $7p + q$.
    7. $3p - 2q + r$ take $p - q - r + s$.
    8. $ab + bc - cd$ take $-ab - cd$.
    9. $pq + qr - s$ take $6pq - 3qr + 2s$.
   10. $x^2 - y^2 - z^2$ take $9x^2 - 7y^2 - 3z^2$.
   11. $\frac{1}{2}x^2 - y^2 - \frac{3}{4}z^2$ take $-x^2 - 2y^2 - \frac{1}{2}z^2$.
   12. $\frac{1}{3}ab + 2bc - \frac{1}{4}cd$ take $-\frac{1}{4}ab - \frac{1}{2}bc$.

CHAPTER THREE

MULTIPLICATION AND DIVISION IN ALGEBRA

Multiplication

(1) $ab = a \times b$ or $b \times a$ or ba; this is the same as in arithmetic, where the product is the same no matter in what order the factors are taken.

(2)
$$a^2 = a \times a = aa,$$
$$a^3 = a \times a \times a = aaa,$$
$$\therefore a^2 \times a^3 = aaaaa = a^5$$

where the resulting index is the *sum* of the two indices.

(3) $a(x + y) = a$ times each term inside the brackets
$$= a \text{ times } x + a \text{ times } y$$
$$= ax + ay.$$

Similarly—
$(a + b)(c + d) = a$ times $(c + d) + b$ times $(c + d)$
$$= ac + ad + bc + bd.$$

Compare the above operations with the following arithmetical operation:

$$
\begin{array}{r}
42 \\
36 \\
\hline
252 \\
1\,260 \\
\hline
1\,512
\end{array}
$$

This operation may be represented as—

$$(40 + 2)(30 + 6) = 30 \text{ times } (40 + 2) + 6 \text{ times } (40 + 2)$$
$$= 1\ 200 + 60 + 240 + 12$$
$$= 1\ 260 + 252$$
$$= 1\ 512.$$

From this it is evident that the multiplication process is really the same in both arithmetic and algebra.

(4) Since $+$ and $-$ enter into algebraical operations, we shall meet in the course of multiplication with the following:

(a) $+$ quantity $\times$ $+$ quantity gives what sign?
(b) $+$,, $\times$ $-$,,   ,,   ,,
(c) $-$,, $\times$ $+$,,   ,,   ,,
(d) $-$,, $\times$ $-$,,   ,,   ,,

Consider $+$ and $-$ as representing, as before, *opposite directions*. Then:

(a) $+5 \times +5$ must $= 5$ positive units taken 5 times in the positive direction, which $= +25$. Hence $+ \times + = +$.

(b) $+5 \times -5$. Here 5 positive units taken 5 times gives $+25$, but taking account of the change of direction indicated by the $-$ sign, $+25$ becomes -25. Hence a positive quantity $\times$ a negative quantity $=$ a negative quantity.

(c) $-5 \times +5$ is evidently the same thing as $+5 \times -5$.

(d) -5×-5, as in (b), indicates that -5 is to be taken 5 times and the sign changed. But -5 taken 5 times $= -25$, and changing the sign we get $+25$. Hence $- \times - = +$.

Combining these results, we have:

(1) $+ \times + \text{ gives}$ $\left.\right\} +.$
    $- \times - \quad,,$

(2) $+ \times - \quad,,$ $\left.\right\} -.$
    $- \times + \quad,,$

Putting this into words, we have the *Rule of Signs* in multiplication:

(1) The product of two terms with *like* signs is *positive*.
(2) The product of two terms with *unlike* signs is *negative*.

Or, in an easily remembered form:

Like signs give $+$.
Unlike signs give $-$.

Example 1.

$$4ab^2 \times 2abc \begin{bmatrix} = 4 \times a \times b \times b \times 2 \times a \times b \times c \\ = 4 \times 2 \times a \times a \times b \times b \times b \times c \\ = 8 \times a^2 \times b^3 \times c \end{bmatrix}$$
$$= 8a^2b^3c.$$

The working in brackets is only explanatory. The product can be got at once.

Example 2.

$$3abc \times - 2b^2c^3 \times - 4a^2.$$

Here the signs of the first two quantities give $-$, and this sign, taken along with the $-$ of the last quantity, gives $+$. Hence the product $= 24a^3b^3c^4$.

Example 3.

$$\begin{array}{l} a^2 - 2ab + b^2. \\ a - b \\ \hline a^3 - 2a^2b + ab^2 \\ \quad - a^2b + 2ab^2 - b^3 \\ \hline a^3 - 3a^2b + 3ab^2 - b^3 \end{array}$$

In Example 3 we multiply the multiplicand by a, which gives $a^3 - 2a^2b + ab^2$; then we multiply it by $-b$, which gives $-a^2b + 2ab^2 - b^3$. When multiplying by $-b$, we take care to place like quantities in the same column, thus $2ab^2$ under ab^2, etc. Then we add just as in Arithmetic.

EXERCISE 4

Multiply:

1. abc by $2a^2b^2c^3$.
2. x^2y^2 by $-2x^2y^3z$.
3. $x + y$ by x^2.
4. $x^2 + 2xy + y^2$ by x^2.
5. $a + b + c$ by $a + b$.
6. $a^2 + 2ab + b^2$ by $a + b$.
7. $3x^2 - y^2$ by $x^2 + y$.
8. $a - b - c$ by $a^2 - b^2$.
9. $x + y$ by $x^2 - y^2$.
10. $-x^2 + y^2$ by $-x + y$.
11. $a^2 - 2ab + b^2$ by $a^2 + 2ab + b^2$.
12. $a - 2b + 1$ by $2a + b + 1$.
13. $\frac{1}{2}x^2 - \frac{1}{2}y^2$ by $\frac{1}{4}x^2 + \frac{1}{2}y^2$.
14. $\frac{1}{2}xy - \frac{1}{2}xz$ by $y^2 + z^2$.
15. $x^3 - y^3$ by $x^3 + y^3$.

Division

The process of algebraic division is exactly the same as in Arithmetic, as may be shown by the following:

$$16)542(33\tfrac{7}{8}$$
$$\underline{48}$$
$$62$$
$$\underline{48}$$
$$\tfrac{14}{16} = \tfrac{7}{8}.$$

B

This process in the extended form is—

$$16) 500 + 40 + 2(31\tfrac{1}{4} + 2\tfrac{1}{2} + \tfrac{1}{8} = 33\tfrac{7}{8}$$

$$\underline{48}$$

$$20$$
$$\underline{16}$$
$$\tfrac{4}{16} = \tfrac{1}{4}$$
$$16)40(2$$
$$\underline{32}$$

$$\tfrac{8}{16} = \tfrac{1}{2}$$
$$2 \div 16 = \tfrac{2}{16} = \tfrac{1}{8}.$$

If the *Rule of Signs* is understood, there should be no difficulty about the signs in division. Since divisor × quotient = dividend, the sign of any term in the quotient will be *such a sign as when multiplied by the sign of the first term of the divisor will give the sign of the first term of the dividend.* Thus, if the divisor is $- x$ and the dividend $- xy$, the sign of the quotient is $+$, which along with the sign of the divisor gives $-$. Thus:

(1) $- x) - xy(+ y$
                     $\underline{- xy}$

                     $\cdot\ \cdot$
                     $\overline{}$

(2) $+ x) - xy(- y$
                     $\underline{- xy}$

                     $\cdot\ \cdot$
                     $\overline{}$

The rule of signs in division is thus seen to be the same as in multiplication, viz.:

Like signs (in divisor and dividend) give $+$ (in the quotient).

Unlike signs (in divisor and dividend) give — (in the quotient).

Example 4.

$$x) \underline{x^2 - 2xy + 3x} \\ x - 2y + 3$$

When the divisor consists of more than one term we proceed, as in Arithmetic, by considering how the *first* part of the divisor goes into the first part of the dividend.

Example 5.

$$x - y) x^2 - 2xy + y^2 (x - y \\ \underline{x^2 - xy} \\ -xy + y^2 \\ \underline{-xy + y^2}$$

. .

Here the result of dividing x^2 by x is x. We then multiply the whole divisor $x - y$ by this quotient x, which gives $x^2 - xy$. We then subtract this and take down the next part of the dividend. Next, the result of dividing $-xy$ by x is $-y$. We then multiply the whole divisor $x - y$ by $-y$ and subtract as before. And so on until there is no remainder. If there is a remainder, notice how we proceed:

$$a - b) a^2 - 2ab + 2b^2 (a - b + \frac{b^2}{a - b} \\ \underline{a^2 - ab} \\ -ab + 2b^2 \\ \underline{-ab + b^2} \\ b^2$$

Here the remainder is b^2, which is not exactly divisible by $a - b$. The division of b^2 by $a - b$ can only be represented by the fraction $\dfrac{b^2}{a - b}$. Now, this fraction must be *added* to the quotient. It would not do to put $b\dfrac{b^2}{a - b}$; for, while $3\frac{1}{2}$ means $3 + \frac{1}{2}$, in Algebra $b\dfrac{b^2}{a - b} = b \times \dfrac{b^2}{a - b}$, and so we must express the answer as above.

EXERCISE 5

Divide:

1. $3a^2$ by a.
2. $4ab$ by $-a$.
3. $8xyz$ by $-2y$.
4. $a^2 - b^2$ by $a - b$.
5. $a^2 + 2ab + b^2$ by $a + b$.
6. $a^2 - 2ab + b^2$ by $a - b$.
7. $a^3 - b^3$ by $a - b$.
8. $a^3 + b^3$ by $a + b$.
9. $a^2 - 2ab + 3b^2$ by $a - b$.
10. $a^3 - 4a^2x + 4ax^2 - x^3$ by $a - x$.
11. $2x^3 - 5x^2y - 9y^3$ by $x - 3y$.
12. $x^6 - a^6$ by $x^2 - ax + a^2$.
13. $x^4 - a^4$ by $x^2 + a^2$.
14. $x^3 - 3x^2y + 3xy^2 - y^3$ by $x - y$.
15. $p^4 - 4p^3q + 6p^2q^2 - 4pq^3 + q^4$ by $p - q$.

CHAPTER FOUR

FACTORS AND MULTIPLES—HIGHEST COMMON FACTOR—LOWEST COMMON MULTIPLE

BEFORE continuing, we shall have to consider the meaning of two words and the operations connected with them. The words are **factor** and **multiple**.

Factors

2 inches are contained in 8 inches four times exactly. 2, then, is said to be a measure or *factor* of 8. Similarly, it is a factor of 4, 6, 10, 12, 14, and so is called a *common factor* of these numbers. Since it is the highest number that is contained exactly in each of the above numbers, it is called their *highest common factor* (H.C.F.).

Multiples

Since the 8 inches above contain the 2 inches an exact number of times, the 8 inches are said to be a *multiple* of the 2 inches. Since 8 contains 2 and 4 exactly, 8 is said to be a *common multiple* of 2 and 4. And since 4 is the lowest number that contains 2 and 4 exactly, 4 is said to be the *lowest common multiple* (L.C.M.) of 4 and 2. Or, again, 15 is said to be the *lowest common multiple* of 5 and 3.

Summing up:

A factor is a number that divides another number exactly.

A common factor is a number that divides each of two or more numbers exactly.

37

The highest common factor is the highest number that divides each of two or more numbers exactly.

A multiple is a number that contains another number an exact number of times.

A common multiple is a number that contains each of two or more numbers exactly.

The lowest common multiple is the smallest number which is exactly divisible by each of two or more given numbers.

The object of finding the H.C.F. and the L.C.M. of two or more numbers is principally to facilitate our work with fractions. Here, however, are types of problems that illustrate a practical use of the ideas of H.C.F. and L.C.M.:

Example 1. Two vessels contain respectively 575 and 840 gallons of liquid; find the vessel of greatest capacity that will completely empty both vats by an exact number of fillings.

Here 5 is the largest number that measures each of the numbers 575 and 840 exactly. Therefore, a five-gallon vessel is the largest that can be used to empty both if none of the liquid is to be left after the last complete vesselful.

Example 2. The sides of a triangular piece of ground measure 1 640, 1 592 and 1 718 feet respectively; find the length of the longest hurdle that can be used to fence it without bending or cutting a hurdle.

Here 2 is the largest number that divides each of the three numbers exactly.

Example 3. A clock is wound up every 6 days, another every 15 days. They are wound up together; how long will it be before this happens again?

Here we want to find the lowest number of days that

will contain both 6 and 15 an exact number of times, and this is evidently the L.C.M.: 30 days.

Example 4. The circumference of two cylinders are 4 feet and 5 feet respectively. What is the smallest length of wire that can be wrapped round each an exact number of times?

Evidently 20 feet of wire is the shortest length that will contain 4 feet and 5 feet exactly.

But most of the "problems" on H.C.F. and L.C.M. set in text-books are somewhat fanciful and only apparently practical; and the real utility, as we have said, of knowing how to find the H.C.F. and L.C.M. of numbers is to facilitate fractional operations. Accordingly, we proceed to show how to find the H.C.F. and L.C.M. of two or more numbers.

Highest Common Factor

Example 5. Suppose we wish to find the H.C.F. of 15, 20, 35. Break up each of the numbers into its simplest factors, that is, factors that cannot be broken up into other factors, thus:

$$15 = 5 \times 3,$$
$$20 = 5 \times 2 \times 2,$$
$$35 = 5 \times 7.$$

From this it is apparent that 5 is the only measure that is found in each, it being found in 15 3 times, in 20 2 × 2 times, i.e., 4 times, in 35 7 times. Hence 5 is the H.C.F. of 15, 20, 35.

Example 6.

$$60 = 5 \times 2 \times 2 \times 3,$$
$$75 = 5 \times 5 \times 3,$$
$$90 = 5 \times 3 \times 3 \times 2.$$

Here 5 occurs once and 3 occurs once in each of the numbers, hence the H.C.F. must be 5 × 3 or 15.

Now in ordinary life you rarely meet with fractional work that will necessitate your finding the H.C.F. of large numbers, and hence you may rest assured that the above method will enable you to find in an intelligent way an H.C.F. whenever required.

EXERCISE 6

1. Find the H.C.F. of 8, 10, 12, 16.
2.   ,,   ,,   15, 25, 75, 85.
3.   ,,   ,,   36, 42, 56, 68.
4.   ,,   ,,   12, 34, 48, 60.
5.   ,,   ,,   51, 102, 204, 306.
6.   ,,   ,,   37, 74, 148, 296.

Lowest Common Multiple

Example 7. To find the L.C.M. of two or more numbers.

As in the case of the H.C.F., break up the numbers into their simplest factors. Since the lowest number that contains each of the numbers must contain *all the factors of those numbers*, the L.C.M. will be readily seen by breaking up the numbers into their simplest or lowest factors. Thus:

$$8 = 2 \times 2 \times 2,$$
$$10 = 2 \times 5,$$
$$24 = 2 \times 2 \times 2 \times 3.$$

The L.C.M. must, therefore, contain 2 × 2 × 2, otherwise it would not contain 8 or 24, each of which contains 2 three times. It must also contain 5, for 5 is found in 10; and 3, for 3 is found in 24. Hence the L.C.M. must be 2 × 2 × 2 × 5 × 3, or 120.

Example 8.

$$15 = 5 \times 3,$$
$$25 = 5 \times 5,$$
$$66 = 11 \times 3 \times 2;$$
$$\therefore \text{L.C.M.} = 5 \times 5 \times 3 \times 11 \times 2,$$
$$= 1\,650.$$

A short method of finding the factors is as follows:

$$
\begin{array}{r}
3)\underline{15,\ 25,\ 66} \\
5)\underline{5,\ 25,\ 22} \\
1,\ \ 5,\ 22
\end{array}
$$
$$\therefore \text{L.C.M.} = 3 \times 5 \times 5 \times 22,$$
$$= 1\,650 \text{ as above.}$$

In this method we choose convenient factors, 3 and 5, and divide them in turn into any of the given numbers which are multiples, leaving non-multiples unchanged. This process may cease as soon as we have left a series of numbers with no common factors, as 1, 5, 22 in the example. The L.C.M. is then found by multiplying the factors and these remaining numbers together.

EXERCISE 7

1. Find the L.C.M. of 3, 4, 5, 6.
2. ,,   ,,   7, 9, 10, 12.
3. ,,   ,,   8, 12, 16, 18.
4. ,,   ,,   12, 15, 18, 21.
5. ,,   ,,   13, 39, 78.
6. ,,   ,,   24, 56, 128, 39.

METHODS OF SHORTENING MULTIPLICATION AND DIVISION

MULTIPLICATION and Division occur so often in all our calculations that one is glad to shorten the work by any device possible. Although continued practice will enable one to form short ways of one's own, there are one or two that it is well to point out here.

1. Multiplication by Factors

This method may be explained thus: 114×28 means 114 taken 28 times, or 28 groups of 114. Now, since $28 = 7 \times 4$ (where 7 and 4 are *factors* of 28), the number in 28 *groups of* 114 = the number in 4 *groups of* 114 *taken 7 times*, or the number in 7 *groups of* 114 *taken 4 times*.

Hence $114 \times 28 = (1)\ (114 \times 7) \times 4$, or
$$(2)\ (114 \times 4) \times 7.$$

$$(1) = 798 \times 4$$
$$= 3\ 192.$$

$$(2) = 456 \times 7$$
$$= 3\ 192.$$

In actual practice all that would be put down would be 798, 3 192; 456, 3 192. By this method we always save ourselves the *addition* operation of the ordinary method.

Thus, ordinary method:

$$\begin{array}{r} 912 \\ 2\ 28 \\ \hline 3\ 192 \end{array}$$

2. Division by Factors

The method may be explained thus: 5 376 marbles ÷ 48 marbles means that we are to find how many groups of 48 there are in 5 376. Now, 48 = 6 × 8. Therefore, if we first divide 5 376 by 8 we shall get the number of *groups* containing 8 marbles. Then if we divide this *number of groups* (of 8) by 6, we shall have a certain number of *groups of* 6, each containing 8 marbles; that is, *groups of* 48.

Example 1.   10 368 ÷ 72.

$$9)\underline{10\ 368}$$
$$8)\underline{1\ 152}\text{ groups of 9.}$$
$$144\text{ groups of (8 groups of 9);}$$

that is, 144 groups of 72.

Notice how remainders are treated.

Example 2.   8 573 921 ÷ 63.

$$9)\underline{8\ 573\ 921}$$
$$7)\underline{952\ 657}\text{ groups of 9, and 8 units over.}$$
$$136\ 093\text{ groups of (7 containing 9 units each),}$$
$$\text{and 6 groups of 9 over.}$$

6 groups of 9 = 54, and this added to the previous remainder of 8 units makes altogether 62 units.

Hence the rule: if there is a remainder after dividing by the second factor, *multiply this remainder by the first factor, and add to it the remainder (if any) after the division by the first factor.*

Example 3.   7 423 979 ÷ 84.

$$12)\underline{7\ 423\ 979}$$
$$7)\underline{618\ 664}\text{ and 11 over.}$$
$$88\ 380\text{ and 4 over.}$$

Thus the remainder is $(4 \times 12) + 11$, or 59.

3. Multiplication by Any One of the Numbers from 11 to 19

The following short method should be known and used by the student. For example:

$$45\,672 \times 17.$$

First consider the ordinary method:

$$
\begin{array}{r}
45\,672 \\
17 \\
\hline
319\,704 \\
456\,72 \\
\hline
776\,424 \\
\end{array}
$$

In this example it will be noticed that the second item in the final addition is 456 72 (short for 456 720), the same as the original multiplicand. Thus the multiplication by 7 and the addition may both be included in the following mental process:

7 times 2 = 14; **4** and carry 1.

7 ,,   7 = 49, and 1 carried = 50, and 2 = 52; **2** and carry 5.

7 ,,   6 = 42, and 5 carried = 47, and 7 = 54; **4** and carry 5.

7 ,,   5 = 35, and 5 carried = 40, and 6 = 46; **6** and carry 4.

7 ,,   4 = 28, and 4 carried = 32, and 5 = 37; **7** and carry 3.

3 and 4 are **7**.

The multiplication is therefore performed in a single line.

Example 4.

$$\begin{array}{r} 845\,679 \\ 18 \\ \hline 15\,222\,222 \end{array}$$

Reduced metal process:

$$\left. \begin{array}{l} \text{Eight 9's 72} \\ \phantom{\text{Eight}} ,, \quad \text{7's 56, 63, 72} \\ \phantom{\text{Eight}} ,, \quad \text{6's 48, 55, 62} \\ \phantom{\text{Eight}} ,, \quad \text{5's 40, 46, 52} \\ \phantom{\text{Eight}} ,, \quad \text{4's 32, 37, 42} \\ \phantom{\text{Eight}} ,, \quad \text{8's 64, 68, 72} \\ \phantom{\text{Eight}} \quad \text{8 and 7 15} \end{array} \right\} = 15\,222\,222.$$

4. Multiplication by Algebraic Means

(*a*) It will be easily seen, since $9 = 10 - 1$, that $9x = 10x - 1x$, where x represents any number. Thus

$$9 \times 38 = 10 \times 38 - 1 \times 38 = 380 - 38 = 342.$$

The same method can be used for multiplication of any number by raising it to the next multiple of 10 or 100.

Note that $\quad 8 = 10 - 2$ and $8x = 10x - 2x$
$$97 = 100 - 3 \text{ and } 97x = 100x - 3x$$

and also $\quad 198 = 200 - 2$ and $198x = 200x - 2x$.

Example 5. Multiply 129 by 293

$$\begin{aligned} 129 \times 293 &= 300 \times 129 - 7 \times 129 \\ &= 38\,700 - 903 \\ &= 37\,797 \end{aligned}$$

(*b*) We have shown earlier that

$$(a - b)(c - d) = ac + bd - bc - ad.$$

This can be used in ordinary multiplication as follows:

Example 6. Multiply 129 by 293.

$$129 = 130 - 1$$
$$293 = 300 - 7$$

Let $a = 130$, $b = 1$, $c = 300$ and $d = 7$.
Then $129 \times 293 = (130 - 1)(300 - 7)$
$$= 130 \times 300 + 1 \times 7 - 1 \times 300 - 130 \times 7$$
$$= 39\,000 + 7 - 300 - 910$$
$$= 39\,007 - 1\,210$$
$$= 37\,797$$

The reader should compare this solution with Example 5.

5. Multiplication and Division by 10, 100, 1 000, etc.; 25, 75, 125

To multiply any number by 10 simply add 0 or a "nought" to the right hand; to multiply by 100 add two "noughts"; to multiply by 1000 add three "noughts", and so on. Thus, $415 \times 10 = 4\,150$, $415 \times 100 = 41\,500$, etc.

To divide any number by 10 cut off the figure farthest to the right; this will be the remainder. Thus, $415 \div 10 = 41$ and 5 over.

To divide by 100 cut off the two figures farthest to the right, and so on.

Example 5. $8\,762 \div 100 = 87$ and 62 over.
$8\,762 \div 1\,000 = 8$ and 762 over.

This will receive further explanation when we come to deal with decimal fractions.

Since $25 = 100 \div 4$, we can multiply a number by 25 by adding two " noughts " to the number and dividing by 4. Thus:

$$87\,432 \times 25$$
$$4)8\,743\,200$$
$$\overline{2\,185\,800}$$

Since $75 = 3 \times 25$, to multiply by 75 we can first multiply by 25 as above and then multiply the result by 3.

Since $125 = 1\,000 \div 8$, to multiply by 125 we add three "noughts" to the number and divide by 8. Thus:

$$752\,398 \times 125$$
$$8)752\,398\,000$$
$$\overline{94\,049\,750}$$

The corresponding divisions by 25, 75 and 125 must be left alone at this point, as they involve difficulties which have to be explained later on.

The above are only a few examples of what can be done to lighten the labour of calculation. The student is advised to study carefully the worked examples throughout this book, where he will meet with further illustrations of short processes, and to look out for and practise short methods himself.

EXERCISE 8

1. If one factor of a number is 11 and the other factor is 4, what is the number?
2. If one factor of a number is 12 and the other factor 7, what is the number?
3. If one factor of 39 is 3, what is the other factor?
4. If 75 is a product of two factors, one of which is 3, what is the other factor?
5. If 128 is the dividend and 4 the divisor, what is the quotient?
6. If 84 is the divisor and 3 the quotient, what is the dividend?
7. If the dividend is 876 and the quotient is 4, find the divisor.
8. If the divisor is 4, quotient 9, and remainder 2, what is the dividend?

9. If $5 \times A = 30$, what is the value of A?
10. If $16 \times P = 48$, what is the value of P?
11. If $36 = 6 \times P$, what is the value of P?
12. If $84 = P \times 3$, what is the value of P?

Multiply, by the method of *factors*:

13. 17 895 by 16, 35, 49, 72.
14. 318 246 by 15, 63, 108.

Multiply:

15. 942 793 by 10, 100, 1 000, 10 000.
16. 7 423 by 13, 14, 15, 16, 17, 18, 19.
17. 89 579 by 25, 75, 125.

Divide by the method of *factors*:

18. 18 456 by 15, 18, 24, 72.
19. 94 273 by 16, 22, 27, 108.
20. Divide 98 456 by 10, 100, 1 000, 10 000.

CHAPTER SIX

THE USE OF BRACKETS

SUPPOSE we want to express the difference between a and the sum of b and c, we may do so by the following:

$$a - (b + c) \text{ or } (b + c) - a.$$

Now, suppose we wish to express the difference between these two expressions, we do so by the following form:

$$\{a - (b + c)\} - \{(b + c) - a\}.$$

The first expression $= a - b - c$ (according to the rule of signs in subtraction). The second expression $= b + c - a$. The difference between the two may then be expressed as $(a - b - c) - (b + c - a)$, and this form in turn becomes, by the rule of signs, $a - b - c - b - c + a$, which $= 2a - 2b - 2c$.

In simplifying such expressions it is convenient to begin with the innermost brackets. The following is a more complicated example:

$$
\begin{aligned}
&b - [a - 2\{b - (c + d) - (2a - b)\} - 3a - b]\\
&= b - [a - 2\{b - c - d - 2a + b\} - 3a - b]\\
&= b - [a - 2b + 2c + 2d + 4a - 2b - 3a - b]\\
&= b - a + 2b - 2c - 2d - 4a + 2b + 3a + b\\
&= -5a + 3a + 6b - 2c - 2d\\
&= -2a + 6b - 2c - 2d.
\end{aligned}
$$

Consider this last result; 2 is evidently a factor of each term, and we can therefore express the result in the following form:

$$2(-a + 3b - c - d),$$

where the bracket shows that each term inside is to be multiplied by 2.

But if we put the minus sign *outside* the bracket, then we must *change each sign inside the bracket*, otherwise the original expression would be altered in value. Thus, suppose we put the expression into the form—

$$- 2(a + 3b - c - d),$$

this, when the bracket is removed, becomes—

$$- 2a - 6b + 2c + 2d,$$

which is different from the original expression. The correct expression must be

$$- 2(a - 3b + c + d).$$

Next, suppose we want to group the four terms in two, taking the first two as the first term and the second two as the second term. We do so as follows:

$$- 2(a - 3b) - 2(c + d).$$

The proof that we have not altered the *value* of the original expression may be had by removing the brackets, that is, by multiplying $- 2$ into each term of the first bracket and $- 2$ into each term of the second bracket, thus:

$$- 2 \times a = - 2a; \; - 2 \times - 3b = + 6b;$$
$$- 2 \times c = - 2c; \; - 2 \times + d = - 2d.$$

From what has been already said it can be seen that the terms of an expression can be combined and bracketed in any way, provided we *change the signs* inside a bracket *when it is preceded by a minus sign*. When it is preceded by a plus sign there is no change.

Example 1. Bracket the terms of the following expression in pairs:

$$3a - 9b + c - d - 2a + 6d$$
$$= (3a - 9b) + (c - d) - (2a - 6d),$$
$$\text{or } 3(a - 3b) + (c - d) - 2(a - 3d).$$

EXERCISE 9

Simplify:

1. $(a + b) - (c + d)$.
2. $2(a - b) - 3(c - d)$.
3. $-(a - b) - (c - d)$.
4. $-2(a - b) + (c - d)$.
5. $a - \{a - (b + c) - 2a\}$.
6. $x - (\frac{1}{2}x + \frac{1}{5}x + \frac{1}{10}x)$.
7. $p - \{q - (r + s - p)\}$.
8. $x - [y - (z + x) - \{2x - (y + z)\}]$.
9. $2p - 2[q - \{r - (s + p)\} - 3q]$.
10. $2\{ab - (cd - ef) - 2(ab - cd)\}$.

Bracket the terms of the following expressions in pairs:

11. $-p - q - r + s$.
12. $2p - q + r - s$.
13. $-xy - yz - p - 2q + r - s$.
14. $6ab - 2bc - 3cd - 4de - 5ef + 6fg$.
15. $-p + q + 2r - s - t + w$.
16. $-2p - 4q - r + s - 2t - 2w$.

CHAPTER SEVEN

EVALUATING ALGEBRAIC EXPRESSIONS

EXAMPLES of how to evaluate algebraic expressions.

Example 1. Given $a = 5$, $b = 4$, $c = 3$, $d = 1$, find the value of $6a + 2b - (c^2 + 2d)$.

The given expression

$$= 30 + 8 - (9 + 2)$$
$$= 38 - 11$$
$$= 27.$$

Example 2. If $a = 7$, $b = 9$, $c = 2$, $d = 0$, find the value of $3a^2 + 2bcd - 3c^2$.

The given expression

$$= (3 \times 49) + (2 \times 9 \times 2 \times 0) - (3 \times 4)$$
$$= 147 + 0 - 12$$
$$= 135.$$

Example 3. If $V = 6$, $t = 15$, $g = 32$, find the value of S where $S = Vt + \frac{1}{2}gt^2$.

$$S = (6 \times 15) + \left(\frac{1}{2} + \overset{16}{32} \times 15^2\right),$$
$$= 90 + (16 \times 225)$$
$$= 90 + 3\,600$$
$$= 3\,690.$$

EXERCISE 10

If $a = 6$, $b = 4$, $c = 10$, $d = 5$, $e = 7$, $f = 12$, $g = 0$, find the values of:

1. $3ab + 2bc - c^2 - de$.
2. $a^2 + b^2 - c + de$.

3. $6(a - b) + 3c^2 - (d + e) - fg$.
4. $2b^2 + 3d - abc + e^2$.
5. $\dfrac{a + b + c}{2d}$.
6. $\dfrac{abc + bcd}{6(a + b)}$.

If $V = 5$, $t = 20$, $g = 32$, find the values of S in the following forms:—

7. $S = \dfrac{V^2}{2g}$.
8. $S = Vt - \frac{1}{2}gt^2$

9. If $W = 70$, $V = 120$, and $g = 32$, find the value of $\dfrac{WV^2}{2g}$.

10. If $W = 50\frac{1}{2}$, $V = 86$, and $g = 32$, find the value of $\dfrac{WV^2}{2g}$.

Examples of expressions containing square and other roots.

Example 4. If $a = 8$, $b = 9$, $c = 16$, $d = 8$, $e = 64$, find the value of $\dfrac{3\sqrt{bc} + \sqrt[3]{de}}{2\sqrt[3]{a} - \sqrt[4]{c} + \sqrt[6]{e}}$.

The expression

$$= \frac{3\sqrt{9 \times 16} + \sqrt[3]{8 \times 64}}{2\sqrt[3]{8} - \sqrt[4]{16} + \sqrt[6]{64}}$$

$$= \frac{(3 \times 3 \times 4) + (2 \times 4)}{(2 \times 2) - 2 + 2}$$

$$= \frac{36 + 8}{4}$$

$$= \frac{44}{4} = 11.$$

Example 5. If $a = 4$, $b = 1$, $c = 3$, $d = 9$, $e = 16$, $f = 32$, find the value of $\sqrt[3]{\dfrac{cd}{4\sqrt[4]{e}}} \div \sqrt{\dfrac{ad}{a^3b}}$.

The expression

$$= \sqrt{\frac{27}{4 \times 2}} \div \sqrt{\frac{4 + 9}{64 \times 1}}$$

$$= \frac{3}{2} \div \frac{6}{8}$$

$$= \frac{3}{2} \times \frac{\overset{4}{8}}{\underset{2}{6}}$$

$$= 2.$$

EXERCISE 11

If $a = 16$, $b = 8$, $c = 3$, $d = 1$, $e = 0$, find the value of:

1. $3\sqrt{a} - 2\sqrt[3]{\dfrac{b}{4a}} + 5c^2\sqrt[4]{\dfrac{a}{d}}.$

2. $3\sqrt[3]{b} + 2c^2\sqrt{de} - 3\sqrt[4]{a}.$

3. $\sqrt{\dfrac{1}{ab^2c^2}}.$

4. $(a + b) - \sqrt[5]{2a} + \sqrt{\dfrac{9c^2d^2}{2\sqrt[3]{b}}}.$

5. $5\sqrt[3]{2ad} + \sqrt[4]{\dfrac{a}{2b}} - de^2.$

If $a = \frac{1}{2}$, $b = \frac{1}{3}$, $c = \frac{1}{4}$, $d = 1$, find the value of:

6. $3a - 2b + c^2 - d^2.$

7. $abc + 4\sqrt{\dfrac{1}{c^4}}.$

8. $(a + b)(c + d).$

9. $3(a - b) + \sqrt{c} - ab.$

10. $2a^2 + 3(b - c) + 2cd - \sqrt{b^2}.$

CHAPTER EIGHT

FRACTIONS

ALMOST every problem that the practical man has to face is more easily solved by fractional than by other methods. It is the aim of this book to enable the reader to acquire a practical mastery of fractional operations, and of the various arithmetical rules which, after all, are just so many applications of the theory of fractions.

What do we really mean by the term "fraction"? What is meant by $\frac{1}{2}$ of a yard, $\frac{2}{3}$ of a mile, $\frac{5}{7}$ of a £1, etc.? In the case of $\frac{1}{2}$ of a yard, the meaning is plain to even the most ignorant. And we do not think that anyone who has passed through school life could be found who could not mark off $\frac{1}{2}$ of a yard on a yard-measure. Could the same be said about the practical problem of finding what $\frac{2}{3}$ of a mile is or $\frac{5}{7}$ of £1? Now, $\frac{2}{3}$ and $\frac{5}{7}$ bear the very same kind of meaning as $\frac{1}{2}$. In the case of $\frac{1}{2}$, the meaning evidently is that the yard is regarded as divided into two *equal* parts, and that *one* of these is taken or thought of. In the same way $\frac{2}{3}$ of a mile means that the mile is regarded as divided into three *equal* parts, and that *two* of them are taken. The same with $\frac{5}{7}$. The term "fraction", then, as applied to such expressions as $\frac{1}{2}$, $\frac{2}{3}$, $\frac{5}{7}$, means *one or more equal parts of a thing*.

Improper and Proper Fractions

What is the meaning of such top-heavy-looking expressions as $\frac{9}{7}$, $\frac{16}{5}$, etc.? If a thing is divided into *seven* equal parts, it is impossible to take *nine* of them. Such forms can be called "fractions" only for convenience— they are **improper fractions** as opposed to **proper fractions**, in which the *numerator* is smaller than the *denominator*.

Thus, $\frac{19}{7}$, $\frac{13}{8}$, $\frac{9}{4}$ are *improper* fractions and $\frac{1}{15}$, $\frac{1}{14}$, $\frac{3}{16}$ are *proper fractions*. $\frac{9}{7}$ of £1 must mean $\frac{7}{7}$ of £1, that is the whole £1, and $\frac{2}{7}$ of another £1. And whilst sometimes it is convenient to work with such fractions as $\frac{9}{7}$, $\frac{16}{5}$, yet in practical work these fractions will meet you in the forms $1\frac{2}{7}$ and $3\frac{1}{5}$.

OPERATIONS WITH VULGAR FRACTIONS

Addition and Subtraction of Vulgar Fractions

1. *When the fractions have the same denominators.*

Example 1. Add $\frac{1}{5}$, $\frac{2}{5}$, $\frac{3}{5}$.

Here, as the unit (it may be £1 or 1s., etc.) is divided in each case into 5 equal parts, the sum of the fractions is found by simply adding the numerators, which gives us $\frac{6}{5}$ or $1\frac{1}{5}$, i.e., one unit and one-fifth.

Example 2. From £$\frac{5}{8}$ take £$\frac{3}{8}$.

Here, as the unit £1 is divided in each case into 8 equal parts, the difference of the fractions is found by simply finding the difference of the numerators, which gives us $\frac{2}{8}$ of £1.

2. *When the fractions have different denominators.*

Example 3. Add $\frac{1}{3}$ mile, $\frac{1}{15}$ mile, $\frac{2}{5}$ mile, $\frac{1}{4}$ mile.

Can we, without altering the values of these fractions, convert them into other fractions having the same denominators? The following shows that we can!

Here are three equal straight lines, the first divided into 4 equal parts, the second into 8 equal parts, the third into 12 equal parts. (See Fig. 6.)

It is evident that $\frac{1}{4}$ of the first line is the same length as $\frac{2}{8}$ of the second line and $\frac{3}{12}$ of the third line. In other words, when the denominator is doubled, trebled, etc., the numerator requires to be doubled, trebled, etc., in order to show the same length as before. The doubling has made the parts only *half as large* as they were originally; and to get a fraction equal to the original fraction we must *double* the *number of parts* taken. Note

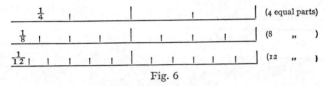

Fig. 6

this fact, then, that *a fraction is not altered in value if both numerator and denominator are multiplied or divided by the same number.* Hence—

$$\left.\begin{array}{l} \frac{1}{3} \text{ mile} = \frac{5}{15} \text{ mile}\\ \frac{1}{15} \quad ,, \quad = \frac{1}{15} \quad ,,\\ \frac{2}{5} \quad ,, \quad = \frac{6}{15} \quad ,, \end{array}\right\} = \frac{12}{15}.$$

We have now to add $\frac{12}{15}$ and $\frac{1}{4}$.

Here it is not quite so evident how to proceed. But the new common denominator must be a multiple of each of the denominators 15 and 4, and, being the *lowest* common denominator (we always want the *lowest* for convenience), must therefore be the lowest common multiple of the given denominators. Find, then, the L.C.M. of 15 and 4. It is 60. $\frac{12}{15}$, then, is to be converted into a fraction whose denominator is 60; that is, a fraction whose denominator is 4 times the original denominator. Thus on multiplying the denominator and numerator by 4 we obtain $\frac{48}{60}$. The same process with $\frac{1}{4}$ gives us $\frac{15}{60}$. Addition of $\frac{48}{60}$ and $\frac{15}{60}$ gives us $\frac{63}{60}$. This, on dividing the numerator and denominator by 3, gives us $\frac{21}{20}$ or $1\frac{1}{20}$.

Example 4.

$$\tfrac{1}{6} + \tfrac{1}{9} + \tfrac{1}{18} + \tfrac{1}{4} + \tfrac{2}{5}.$$

L.C.M. of denominators = 180.

Hence the whole expression

$$= \tfrac{30}{180} + \tfrac{20}{180} + \tfrac{10}{180} + \tfrac{45}{180} + \tfrac{72}{180},$$

or, more shortly,

$$\frac{30 + 20 + 10 + 45 + 72}{180} = \frac{177}{180}.$$

Example 5.

$$2\tfrac{1}{2} + \tfrac{3}{4} + \tfrac{7}{8} + \tfrac{5}{11}.$$

Leave the 2 out of account for the present and deal with the fractions.

L.C.M. of 2, 4, 8, 11 = 88;

$$\therefore 2\tfrac{1}{2} + \tfrac{3}{4} + \tfrac{7}{8} + \tfrac{5}{11}$$
$$= 2\tfrac{44 + 66 + 77 + 40}{88}$$
$$= 2\tfrac{227}{88}$$
$$= 2 + 2\tfrac{51}{88}$$
$$= 4\tfrac{51}{88}.$$

It has been shown that a fraction is not altered in value if both its numerator and denominator are multiplied or divided by the same number.

The process of altering the form of the fraction by *dividing* both numerator and denominator by the same number is called *cancelling*. Its great utility in shortening calculations will appear all through the worked examples of the book. Meanwhile, the following examples will show its utility in the addition and subtraction of fractions:

Example 6. Add $\tfrac{36}{72}$, $\tfrac{15}{180}$, $\tfrac{98}{144}$, $\tfrac{17}{51}$.

Here $\tfrac{36}{72} = \tfrac{1}{2}$, $\tfrac{15}{180} = \tfrac{1}{12}$, $\tfrac{98}{144} = \tfrac{49}{72}$, $\tfrac{17}{51} = \tfrac{1}{3}$; and it is certainly easier to add $\tfrac{1}{2}$, $\tfrac{1}{12}$, $\tfrac{49}{72}$ and $\tfrac{1}{3}$ than to add the fractions in their original form. The L.C.M. of 2, 12, 72 and 3 = 72.

Thus $\frac{1}{2} + \frac{1}{12} + \frac{49}{72} + \frac{1}{3}$
$$= \frac{36 + 6 + 49 + 24}{72}$$
$$= \frac{115}{72}$$
$$= 1\frac{43}{72}$$

Example 7. From the sum of $\frac{19}{38}$ and $\frac{18}{20}$ take $\frac{16}{120}$.

Here $\frac{19}{38} = \frac{1}{2}$, $\frac{18}{20} = \frac{9}{10}$, and $\frac{16}{120} = \frac{2}{15}$, and the expression $\frac{1}{2} + \frac{9}{10} - \frac{2}{15}$ is more easily simplified than the expression $\frac{19}{38} + \frac{18}{20} - \frac{16}{120}$. The reader should complete this problem to obtain the answer $1\frac{4}{15}$.

EXERCISE 12

1. Reduce the following fractions to their simplest forms: $\frac{18}{20}$, $\frac{14}{28}$, $\frac{39}{117}$, $\frac{26}{38}$.

2. What is the difference between the following pairs of fractions: $\frac{3}{8}$ and $\frac{6}{16}$; $\frac{3}{4}$ and $\frac{4}{5}$; $\frac{8}{9}$ and $\frac{7}{8}$?

3. Add $£\frac{1}{3}$, $£\frac{1}{2}$, $£\frac{7}{8}$, $£\frac{3}{16}$.

4. Add $2\frac{3}{4}$ tons, $\frac{5}{6}$ ton, $\frac{7}{16}$ ton, $\frac{4}{5}$ ton.

5. Two men own $\frac{1}{4}$ and $\frac{1}{7}$ of a business respectively. How much of the whole business do they own between them?

6. Which is the larger of the following pairs of fractions: $\frac{3}{7}$ or $\frac{4}{9}$; $\frac{12}{13}$ or $\frac{11}{14}$? (If the fractions are changed into others having the same denominators, then the fraction with the larger numerator must be the larger.)

7. From the sum of $\frac{1}{3}$ and $\frac{1}{6}$ take $\frac{1}{15}$.

8. A sum of money is divided among three persons, A, B, C. A received $\frac{3}{16}$ of it; B receives $\frac{3}{8}$ of it. What fraction does C receive? (Evidently 1 *less* the sum of $\frac{3}{16}$ and $\frac{3}{8}$. Notice that 1 can be represented by $\frac{2}{2}$, $\frac{3}{3}$, $\frac{10}{10}$, etc., etc.)

9. Arrange in order of magnitude the fractions $\frac{4}{7}$, $\frac{5}{9}$, $\frac{3}{4}$, $\frac{7}{8}$, $\frac{8}{9}$ and $\frac{6}{10}$.

10. A cistern can be filled by one pipe in 15 minutes, and by another in 20 minutes; in what time would both together fill it? (The pipe that fills the cistern in 15 minutes puts in $\frac{1}{15}$ in 1 minute.)

11. Two pipes empty a cistern in 8 and 10 hours respectively, and a third pipe fills it in 6 hours; in what time will the cistern be emptied if all three pipes are opened at the same time?

12. I have read 50 pages of a book containing 205 pages. What fraction of the book have I read, and what fraction have I still to read? (The whole unit—the book—is divided into 205 equal parts or pages, and 50 of them have been read.)

Multiplication of Vulgar Fractions

1. *To multiply a fraction by a whole number.*

Example 8. $\frac{3}{8} \times 2$.

Here $\frac{3}{8}$ means that the unit is divided into 8 equal parts and that 3 of these parts are taken. Therefore, 3 of these equal parts taken 2 times will $= 6$ eighth parts; or

$$\frac{3}{8} \times 2 = \frac{6}{8}, \text{ or } 6 \text{ eighths.}$$

Hence rule: Multiply *numerator* by the whole number.

2. *To multiply a fraction by a fraction.*

Example 9. $\frac{5}{8} \times \frac{2}{3}$, or, what is the same thing, $\frac{2}{3}$ of $\frac{5}{8}$.

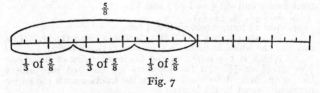

$\frac{1}{3}$ of $\frac{5}{8}$ $\frac{1}{3}$ of $\frac{5}{8}$ $\frac{1}{3}$ of $\frac{5}{8}$

Fig. 7

Take a line divided (1) into 8 equal parts, (2) into 24 equal parts. Then from the diagram it will be seen that $\frac{1}{3}$ of $\frac{5}{8}$ is the same as $\frac{5}{24}$.

Similarly, $\frac{1}{3}$ of $\frac{2}{8} = \frac{2}{24}$, $\frac{1}{3}$ of $\frac{5}{6} = \frac{5}{18}$, etc. That is, $\frac{1}{3}$ of the fraction is got by *increasing* the denominator 3 times. Thus:

$$\frac{1}{3} \text{ of } \frac{5}{8} = \frac{5}{24};$$
$$\text{therefore } 2 \text{ times } \frac{1}{3} \text{ of } \frac{5}{8} = 2 \text{ times } \frac{5}{24}$$
$$= \frac{10}{24} \text{ (by first case).}$$

The diagram shows that this is the case.

Hence rule: Multiply numerators for the new numerator, and denominators for the new denominator.

EXERCISE 13

Find the values of:

1. 5 halves.
2. 3 sevenths.
3. 5 times $\frac{2}{3}$.
4. $8 \times \frac{3}{12}$.
5. $9 \times \frac{1}{4}$.
6. $\frac{1}{7}$ of 4.
7. $\frac{3}{7}$ of 15.
8. $\frac{2}{5}$ of 5.
9. $\frac{2}{15}$ of £75.
10. $\frac{5}{8}$ of 1 mile.
11. 7 half yards.
12. 9 two-fifths of 1 ton.

13. $\frac{1}{2}$ of $\frac{1}{2}$.
14. $\frac{1}{4}$ of $\frac{1}{4}$.
15. $\frac{3}{5}$ of $\frac{1}{3}$.
16. $\frac{3}{4}$ of $\frac{5}{9}$.
17. $\frac{1}{2}$ of $\frac{3}{4}$ of 1 yd.
18. $\frac{2}{3}$ of $\frac{5}{16}$ of 1 mile.
19. $\frac{3}{4}$ of $2\frac{1}{2}$.
20. $\frac{5}{8}$ of $7\frac{1}{2}$ tons.
21. $\frac{3}{5}$ of $40\frac{1}{2}$ sq. yds.
22. $\frac{7}{8}$ of £35 10s.
23. $\frac{9}{10}$ of $35\frac{1}{4}$ acres.
24. $\frac{4}{7}$ of $3\frac{1}{2}$ guineas.

Division of Vulgar Fractions

1. *To divide a fraction by a whole number.*

Example 10. $\frac{5}{8}$ divided by 4, or expressed thus: $\frac{5}{8} \div 4$.

We have already seen that in *multiplying* $\frac{5}{8}$ by 4 we simply multiply the numerator and leave the denominator unchanged. Hence in dividing $\frac{5}{8}$ by 4, the direct way would be to *divide* the numerator by 4 and leave the denominator unchanged. Now, were the fraction $\frac{12}{8}$, this would easily be done, and we should have $\frac{12}{8} \div 4 = \frac{3}{8}$. But in the case of $\frac{5}{8}$ and other fractions whose numerators are not exactly divisible by the divisor, this method is not so convenient. In the case of $\frac{5}{8}$ we should have as a result $\frac{\frac{5}{4}}{8}$, or $1\frac{1}{4}$ eighths. But to divide the numerator of a fraction has the same effect on the fraction as to multiply the denominator; that is, doubling or halving the *number* of parts taken is the same thing as halving or doubling the *size* of the parts. And so to divide $\frac{5}{8}$ by 4 it is more convenient to multiply the denominator by 4, that is, we multiply the fraction by the *divisor inverted*, or turned upside down.

Illustrations: $\frac{3}{4} \div 7 = \frac{3}{28}$; $\frac{5}{6} \div 3 = \frac{5}{18}$; $\frac{2}{5} \div 6 = \frac{2}{30} = \frac{1}{15}$.

2. *To divide a fraction by a fraction.*

Example 11. $\frac{3}{8} \div \frac{2}{5}$
$$\frac{3}{8} \div 2 = \frac{3}{16} \text{ (first case).}$$

But the real divisor is not 2 but $\frac{2}{5}$, that is, only $\frac{1}{5}$ of 2; hence the result $\frac{3}{16}$ will be 5 times too small, therefore we must increase it 5 times, that is, we must take $\frac{3}{16}$ 5 times, that is $\frac{15}{16}$. Hence rule:

To divide a fraction by a fraction, *invert the divisor, and multiply* (as in multiplication of fractions).

Example 12. (1) $\frac{3}{4} \div \frac{2}{3} = \frac{3}{4} \times \frac{3}{2} = \frac{9}{8}$.
(2) $\frac{5}{6} \div \frac{7}{8} = \frac{5}{6} \times \frac{8}{7} = \frac{40}{42} = \frac{20}{21}$.

The same rule will, of course, apply in dividing a whole number by a fraction.

Example 13. (1) $10 \div \frac{1}{2} = 10 \times 2 = 20$.
(2) $5 \div \frac{3}{4} = 5 \times \frac{4}{3} = \frac{20}{3} = 6\frac{2}{3}$.

EXERCISE 14

Find the values of:
1. $\frac{5}{8}$ divided by 3.
2. $\frac{5}{6} \div 7$.
3. $\frac{4}{15} \div 5$.
4. $\frac{8}{12} \div 6$.
5. $\frac{13}{14} \div 5$.
6. $10 \div \frac{1}{4}$.
7. $16 \div \frac{3}{4}$.
8. $\frac{5}{7} \div \frac{6}{8}$.
9. $\frac{3}{8} \div \frac{7}{5}$.

10. If ⅝ of a piece of property is divided equally between three people, what fraction of the property does each get?

11. How many three-quarters of a yard are there in 60 yards?

12. Along a road 1 260 yards long posts are to be placed 3½ yards apart; how many posts will be required?

13. A piece of wire is 51½ yards long; how many lengths of ¼ yard can be cut off it?

14. How often will a coil of rope 205 yards long go round a cylinder 1½ yards in circumference?

CHAPTER NINE

SIMPLE ALGEBRAIC FRACTIONS

A VERY little knowledge of algebraic fractions goes a long way in ordinary practical requirements, and what knowledge is needed is so very like that in Arithmetic that the student has really very little new to learn. We shall treat of the processes in as short a way as possible.

1. Reduction

This is performed as in Arithmetic by *cancelling*, thus:

(1) $\dfrac{3a}{9ab} = \dfrac{1}{3b}$ cancelling $3a$, the common factor of numerator and denominator.

(2) $\dfrac{\overset{4}{\cancel{16}}x^2\cancel{y^2}z^3}{\underset{y}{\cancel{4y^3}}} = \dfrac{4x^2z^3}{y}.$

2. Addition and Subtraction

Example 1. $\qquad \dfrac{a}{b} + \dfrac{2a}{3b}.$

As in Arithmetic, first express all the fractions as fractions with the *same denominator*, then add the numerators, thus:

$$\frac{3a}{3b} + \frac{2a}{3b} = \frac{5a}{3b}, \text{ or } \frac{3a + 2a}{3b} = \frac{5a}{3b}.$$

Example 2.

$$\frac{x}{4} + \frac{x}{8} + \frac{2x}{3} = \frac{6x + 3x + 16x}{24} = \frac{25x}{24}.$$

Example 3.

$$\frac{7x}{8} \times \frac{x}{12} - \frac{x}{9} = \frac{63x + 6x - 8x}{72} = \frac{69x - 8x}{72} = \frac{61x}{72}.$$

3. Multiplication and Division

As in Arithmetic, thus:

Example 4.

$$\frac{3xy}{2} \times \frac{7x^2y^2}{3x^2} = \frac{7xy^3}{2}.$$

Example 5.

$$\frac{b^2}{4} \times \frac{abc}{2b^3} \div \frac{3b^2x}{4} = \frac{b^2}{4} \times \frac{abc}{2b^3} \times \frac{4}{3b^2x} \text{ (divisor inverted)}$$

$$= \frac{ac}{6b^2x}.$$

Exercise 15

Reduce the following to their simplest forms:

1. $\dfrac{5x}{20y}$, $\dfrac{14x^2}{2xy}$, $\dfrac{18x^3}{36y^3}$.

2. $\dfrac{abc}{b^2}$, $\dfrac{cde}{d}$, $\dfrac{p^2q^2}{q^3}$.

3. $\dfrac{6pqr}{2q^2r^2}$, $\dfrac{18lmn}{l^2}$, $\dfrac{16s^2v}{4v^3}$.

4. $\dfrac{x}{2} + \dfrac{x}{3}$.

5. $\dfrac{14x}{3} + \dfrac{x}{8}$.

6. $\dfrac{m}{8} - \dfrac{n}{12}$.

7. $\dfrac{pq}{r} + \dfrac{2pq}{r^2}$.

8. $\dfrac{x}{3} + \dfrac{x}{6} - \dfrac{x}{8}$.

9. $\dfrac{2x}{3} + \dfrac{3x}{4} - \dfrac{4x}{5}$.

10. $\dfrac{a^2b^2}{3} + \dfrac{2a^2b^2}{9} - a^2b^2$.

11. $\dfrac{3xy}{2} \times 7y^2 \times \dfrac{8}{5x}$.

12. $\dfrac{12pq}{p^2} \times \dfrac{3p^3}{2} \div \dfrac{4p^4}{3}$.

13. $\dfrac{abc}{m} \times \dfrac{b^2}{n} \div pq$.

14. $\dfrac{a^3}{b^3} \times \dfrac{b^3}{a^3} \div (-ab)$.

15. $\dfrac{15b^2}{40} \times \dfrac{2px}{p^2} \times 3bx$.

16. $\dfrac{ab}{c^2} \times (-30a^2b^2) \times \dfrac{7c^3}{b} \div b^3$.

C

CHAPTER TEN

DECIMALS

CONTINENTAL people are saved the trouble of dealing with fractions having different denominators by their use of fractions having *always* as their denominators 10, 100, 1 000, etc. Let us explain a little further.

In our arithmetical notation, or method of numbering 1 111 means 1 000 and 100, and 10 and 1; or arranged thus:

$$
\begin{array}{r}
1\ 000 \\
100 \\
10 \\
1 \\
\hline
1\ 111
\end{array}
$$

In the above number we consider each figure as being *ten* times as valuable as the neighbouring right-hand figure. Similarly, 5 643 = 5 000 + 600 + 40 + 3, that is, 3 + 10 times 4 + 100 times 6 + 1 000 times 5.

Now, supposing we reckon from the unit's place *towards the right*, the first place to the right of the unit would be *one-tenth* of the value of the unit's place, the second place would be one-tenth of the value of the first place, and so on. Then if we insert some mark (a dot) to distinguish between the unit and the tenth of the unit, the expression 111·111 will mean 100 + 10 + 1 + $\frac{1}{10}$ + $\frac{1}{100}$ + $\frac{1}{1000}$.

But such a system of fractions as is here indicated is most useful only where the various weights and measures of commodities are divided into tenths, hundredths, etc. This is the case with the Decimal system of weights and measures, which is employed on the Continent. The full meaning and advantage of the Decimal system of calculation will appear later.

Addition and Subtraction of Decimal Fractions

A decimal fraction is one in which the denominator is 10, 100, 1 000, etc.; that is, 10 or some power of 10. These fractions are simply extensions of the ordinary whole numbers; and their addition, subtraction, multiplication and division are performed in the same way as the addition, etc., of whole numbers.

The following will help you to understand the method of addition and subtraction: First, 3 564·893 means three thousands, five hundreds, six tens, four units, eight tenths, nine hundredths, three thousandths; or expressed thus:

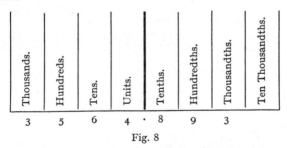

Fig. 8

Consequently, if we wish to add to this any similar number or numbers, all we have to do is to see, as in ordinary addition, that units are placed beneath units, tens beneath tens, tenths beneath tenths and so on. This will be easily done if we take care to *place the decimal points under each other*. The same will hold good with regard to subtraction.

Example 1. Add 5·75, 845·6, 9·305 1, 815·5, 7 192·83, 0·000 05.

$$
\begin{array}{r}
5·75 \\
845·6 \\
9·305\ 1 \\
815·5 \\
7\ 192·83 \\
0·000\ 05 \\
\hline
8\ 868·985\ 15
\end{array}
$$

Example 2. From 815·62 take 75·814.

$$
\begin{array}{r}
815·62 \\
75·814 \\
\hline
739·806
\end{array}
$$

Example 3. From 0·001 take 0·000 09.

$$
\begin{array}{r}
0·001 \\
0·000\ 09 \\
\hline
0·000\ 91
\end{array}
$$

EXERCISE 16

Add together:
1. 0·056, 8·934, 19·84, 17·65.
2. 0·005, 15·6, 81·3, 0·000 9.
3. 14·375, 19·005, 81·652, 17·01.
4. 642·000 5, 9 023·6, 84·000 95, 72·34, 0·000 05.
5. 180·910 2, 1 875·03, 123·123, 0·000 919, 0·01, 0·023, 0·345.

Subtract:
6. 8 from 8·75.
7. 19 from 26·837 05.
8. 113·1 from 115·75.
9. 27·01 from 38·001.
10. 0·000 5 from 0·005.

Multiplication of Decimals

In multiplication you proceed as in the case of whole numbers. The only new thing to notice is the *placing of the decimal point*.

The following will explain:

$$0.5 \times 0.3 = 5 \text{ tenths} \times 3 \text{ tenths},$$
$$= 15 \text{ hundredths},$$
$$= 0.15.$$
$$0.25 \times 0.3 = 25 \text{ hundredths} \times 3 \text{ tenths},$$
$$= 75 \text{ thousandths},$$
$$= 0.075.$$

In this way you will see *that the number of decimal places in the product is always equal to the number in the multiplicand + the number in the multiplier*.

Example 4. 784.623×0.34

$$
\begin{array}{r}
784623 \\
34 \\
\hline
3138492 \\
2353869 \\
\hline
266.77182
\end{array}
$$

Here 3 in the multiplicand is in the third decimal place, and 4 in the multiplier is in the second decimal place; hence the product of 3 by 4 will be in the fifth decimal place; that is, 2 in the product must be five places to the right of the decimal point. Hence the point must be between 6 and 7.

Example 5.   0·000 5 × 0·003

$$\begin{array}{r} 5 \\ 3 \\ \hline 15 \end{array}$$

Here 5 must be in the seventh decimal place, and so 5 "noughts" must be placed between 1 and the point, thus, 0·000 001 5.

Absurd answers often arise from a misplacing of the point. A good way to avoid these is to test your answer if possible by a mental calculation with vulgar fractions. Thus, supposing we have to multiply 0·56 by 12, 0·56 × 12 = 6·72.

Now, 0·56 is almost = $\frac{1}{2}$, and $\frac{1}{2}$ of 12 = 6, which proves that the result 6·72 is correct as far as the whole number is concerned.

Division of Decimals

In dividing one quantity by another when decimals are concerned in one or both, you proceed as in ordinary division. The small difficulty again, as in multiplication, is where to place the point.

First we multiply or divide the divisor by the power of 10 (10, 100, 1 000, etc.) needed to bring the decimal point after the last figure, and of course multiply the dividend also by the same power of 10. As already explained, this can be done by shifting the decimal point in each case the same number of places to right or left.

Thus in finding 845·75 ÷ 25·3, we actually work out 8 457·5 ÷ 253, or in dividing 63 by 0·003 6 we work out 630 000 ÷ 36.

The division then proceeds as usual, and the decimal point can be placed in the quotient by inspection (or common sense). Thus if 7·81, 7 810, 0·007 81 are divided by 4, the decimal places in the quotients clearly have exactly the same positions as they have in the dividends. The quotients are in fact 1·952 5, 1 952·5, 0·001 952 5. If, on the other hand, we had been dividing 2·81, 2 810, 0·002 81 by 4, the decimal points would all have been one place further to the left: 0·702 5, 702·5, 0·000 702 5. (The difference between the two cases is that 7 is greater than 4, while 2 is less.) In these cases with a simple divisor there is no difficulty. The principle is, however, exactly the same when the divisor, instead of being 4, is, for example, 4·736. Thus 7·81 ÷ 4·736 is 1· . . ., and 0·002 81 ÷ 4·736 is 0·000 5 . . .

Example 6. 845·75 ÷ 25·3.

$$
\begin{array}{r}
33\cdot4^2 \\
253)\overline{8\ 457\cdot5} \\
7\ 59 \\
\hline
867 \\
759 \\
\hline
1085 \\
1012 \\
\hline
730 \\
506 \\
\hline
\end{array}
$$

Example 7. 0·356 ÷ 116·4.

$$
\begin{array}{r}
0\cdot003\ 05 \\
1\ 164)\overline{3\cdot560\ 00} \\
3\ 492 \\
\hline
6\ 800 \\
5\ 820 \\
\hline
\end{array}
$$

As a rule there is no point in carrying decimals to more than three or four places. When it comes to measuring tenths, etc., of inches, you can readily see how errors will creep in from the use of defective instruments, from errors of observation and from inaccurate measurements; so that if an error is made in the *first* decimal place you are only increasing it by carrying your calculations beyond this place. The reader should note that in Examples 1 and 2 the answers obtained are correct to one decimal place *less* than the number shown in the answer. This will be explained in more detail later.

In connection with multiplication and division of decimals keep the following well in mind:

First. In multiplying a decimal by 10, 100, etc., it is evident that all we have to do is to move the decimal point *to the right*, one place if multiplying by 10, two places if by 100 and so on. Thus:

$$54 \cdot 26 \times \quad 10 = 542 \cdot 6,$$
$$0 \cdot 005 \times \quad 100 = 0 \cdot 5,$$
$$8 \cdot 6 \times 1\,000 = 8\,600.$$

Second. In dividing a decimal by 10, 100, etc., we move the decimal point *to the left*. Thus:

$$84 \cdot 6 \div \quad 10 = 8 \cdot 46,$$
$$0 \cdot 89 \div \quad 100 = 0 \cdot 008\,9,$$
$$175 \cdot 32 \div 1\,000 = 0 \cdot 175\,32.$$

EXERCISE 17

1. Multiply 81·4 by 0·005.
2. „ 7·1 by 8·35.
3. „ 90·09 by 8·001.
4. „ 0·000 9 by 0·006.
5. „ 1 009·575 by 7·65.
6. „ 0·007 by 1 000.
7. Divide 0·875 by 0·23.
8. „ 91 by 0·005.
9. „ 17·32 by 0·004.

10. Divide 1·001 by 100.
11.   ,,   875 by 0·53.
12.   ,,   150 by 0·150.
13.   ,,   0·008 75 by 25.
14.   ,,   6·15 by 2·3.

15. How many times can 0·015 be subtracted from 853, and what is the remainder?

16. A roller 3·75 ft. in circumference makes 35 revolutions in passing from one end of a bowling green to the other. What is the length of the bowling green?

17. Add together 0·55 of a week, 0·36 of a day and 0·72 of an hour, and express the result in hours.

18. The length of a strip of plate is 16·25 in. long. How many pieces 0·12 in. long can be cut off from it, and what will be the length of the odd bit?

CHAPTER ELEVEN

CALCULATIONS WITH DECIMALS AND FRACTIONS

Discarding of Certain Decimals in Practical Work

IN practical work it is unnecessary to carry the decimal operations to more than one or two decimal places. The result will not be strictly correct; but since at the very best it is impossible to be perfectly exact with our *measurements*, our calculations will not be so far out. In discarding certain of the decimals, therefore, we must simply try to do so with the least possible error. For example, if a result came out as 1·573 6 and we wished to retain only one decimal place, 1·6 would be a more correct result than 1·5, for 0·57 is *nearer* 0·60 than 0·50. Again, if we wished to retain two decimal places, 1·57 would be a more correct result than 1·58, for 0·57 is *nearer* 0·573 than 0·580. The rule, then, we adopt is: (1) to increase the last figure retained by 1 if the next figure is 5 or more than 5; (2) to leave the last figure unchanged if the next figure is below 5.

Example of the application of the idea:

Add 0·572 3, 8·653, 5·429 7, 14·005 3 so as to retain two places of decimals.

Ordinary Method.	Contracted Method.
0·572 3	0·57
8·653	8·65
5·429 7	5·43
14·005 3	14·01
———	———
28·660 3	28·66

Here the *contracted* result differs from the *actual* result by 0·000 3 (28·660 3 *minus* 28·66); that is by $\frac{3}{10000}$.

Contacted methods are also employed in multiplication and division of *long* decimals. As ordinary practical life seldom or never calls for multiplication and division with lengthy decimals, the contracted methods are not included in this volume.

Applications of Fractions

The following examples illustrate some of the methods of dealing with concrete quantities:

Example 1. To express one quantity as the fraction of another, say £5 7s. 6d. of £50.

Just as $\frac{1}{2}$ expresses the fraction which 1 is of 2, or $\frac{3}{4}$ the fraction which 3 is of 4, so $\dfrac{£5\ 7s.\ 6d.}{£50}$ expresses the fraction which £5 7s. 6d. is of £50.

Of course, this fraction must be simplified in order to make it more definite. Thus:

$$\frac{£5\ 7s.\ 6d.}{£50} = \frac{5\frac{3}{8}}{50} = \frac{\frac{43}{8}}{50} = \frac{43}{8} \times \frac{1}{50} = \frac{43}{400}.$$

£5 7s. 6d., then, is $\frac{43}{400}$ of £50.

Example 2. Reduce £3 12s. 6d. to a fraction of £1.

$$\begin{aligned} \text{The fraction} &= \frac{£3\ 12s.\ 6d.}{£1} \\ &= \frac{£3\frac{5}{8}}{£1} \\ &= \frac{29}{8} = 3\frac{5}{8}. \end{aligned}$$

The answer $3\frac{5}{8}$ means that £3 12s. 6d. is $3\frac{5}{8}$ times £1.

Example 3. What fraction of 10$\frac{1}{2}$ miles is 50 yd. 2 ft.?

The fraction $= \dfrac{50 \text{ yd. } 2 \text{ ft.}}{10\frac{1}{2} \text{ miles}}$

$= \dfrac{50\frac{2}{3} \text{ yd.}}{(10\frac{1}{2} \times 1\,760) \text{ yd.}}$

$= \dfrac{\frac{152}{3}}{21 \times 880}$

$= \dfrac{\overset{19}{\cancel{152}}}{3} \times \dfrac{1}{21 \times \underset{110}{\cancel{880}}}$

$= \dfrac{19}{6930}.$

Applications of Decimals

Example 4. What decimal of £5 is £4 6s. 8d.?

The vulgar fraction $= \dfrac{£4 \text{ 6s. 8d.}}{£5}$

$= \dfrac{£4\frac{1}{3}}{£5}$

$= \dfrac{13}{3} \times \dfrac{1}{5}.$

$= \dfrac{13}{15}.$

Therefore the decimal fraction $=$ $0.866 = 0.87$

$$15)\overline{13 \cdot 000}$$
$$\underline{12\ 0}$$
$$1\ 00$$
$$\underline{90}$$
$$100$$
$$\underline{90}$$
$$10$$

Example 5. What decimal is 1d. of £100?

$$\frac{1}{100 \times 240} = \frac{1}{24000}.$$

To simplify the division we consider this as being

$$\frac{0.001}{24}$$

Therefore

$$0.000\ 041\ 66$$
$$24\overline{)0.001\ 000\ 00}$$
$$96$$
$$\overline{}$$
$$40$$
$$24$$
$$\overline{16\ 0}$$
$$14\ 4$$
$$\overline{1\ 60}$$
$$1\ 44$$

$$0.000\ 041\ 66\ \ldots = .000\ 041\ 7.$$

Example 6. To express £5·875 in £ s. d.

$$£5·875$$
$$20$$
$$\overline{}$$
$$\text{s. } 17·500$$
$$12$$
$$\overline{}$$
$$\text{d. } \mathbf{6}·0$$

$$\therefore £5·875 = £5 \text{ 17s. 6d.}$$

The reasoning of the above process is as follows:

(1) 0·875 of £1 = 0·875 of 20s. = 0·875 × 20s.
(2) 0·5 of 1s. = 0·5 of 12d. = 0·5 × 12d.

Example 7. To express any quantity as a decimal of its highest denomination.

These problems are solved by first considering the lowest term and expressing this as a decimal of the next term. This is then expressed as a decimal of the next term, and the process is then continued until the answer is obtained.

1. To express 2 tons 3 cwt. 1 qr. 14 lb. as a decimal of 1 ton.

First consider the lb.

```
28)14
   0·5 qr.
   1·  qr. (added)
 4)1·5
   0·375 cwt.
   3·      ,,  (added)
20)3·375
   0·168 75 tons
   2·      ,,  (added)
   ─────────
   2·168 75 tons
```

Or, more shortly, by putting in the added quantities where the "noughts" are, thus:

```
28)14
 4)  1·5
20)  3·375
     2·168 75
```

2. To express 8 miles 3 fur. 30 yd. 2½ ft. as a decimal of 1 mile.

```
  3)  2·5
11)30·833 yd.
20)  2·803
 8)  3·140 1 fur.
     8·392 5 miles.
```

Both of the above examples might have been worked by the method of example 2, thus:

$$\frac{8 \text{ miles 3 fur. 30 yd. } 2\frac{1}{2} \text{ ft.}}{1 \text{ mile}}, \text{ etc.}$$

Example 8. The following example will perhaps help to explain the decimal method of procedure with *complex* quantities.

To find the value of 2·5 of 1 ton 6 cwt. + 3·125 of 2 qr. 16 lb. + 3·75 of 448 oz.

			Tons.	cwt.	qr.	lb.
⎰ 2·5 of 1 ton	= 2·5		= 2	10	0	0
⎱ 2·5 of 6 cwt.	= 15·0		= 0	15	0	0
⎧ 3·125 of 2 qr.	= 6·250 qr.					
⎪	28					
⎨	————					
⎪	7·00 lb.		= 0	1	2	7
⎩ 3·125 of 16 lb.	= 50·000 lb.		= 0	0	1	22
3·75 of 448 oz.	= 448					
	375					
	16)1 680·00 oz.					
	28)105					
	3 qr. 21 lb.		= 0	0	3	21
			= 3	7	3	22

Exercise 18

1. What fraction is £6 7s. 6d. of £20 7s. 6d.?
2. Reduce 2 cwt. 2 qr. to the fraction of 1 cwt.
3. 5 ft. is what fraction of 10 yd.?
4. What fraction is 15 ac. 3 rd. 20 sq. yd. of 1 sq. mile?
5. Reduce 5 ft. 6 in. to the decimal of 12 ft.
6. Express 17½ cu. ft. as the decimal of 1 cu. yd.
7. What decimal is 5d. of £1?
8. What decimal of a guinea is 6d.?
9. Express as a compound quantity 0·575 of £1 + 0·3 of 1s. + 0·75 of 6d.
10. Find the value of 0·006 25 of a sovereign.
11. Add together 0·125 of £1, 0·75 of 6s., and 0·125 of 6d., and express the result as the decimal of £1.
12. Express £5 17s. 6d. as a decimal of £1.
13. Find the value of 10 miles 150 yd. of telegraph wire at £5 15s. per mile. (Convert both quantities into the decimal form, then multiply and reduce as in examples 6 and 8.)

14. Express 0·5 of 1 lb. as a decimal of 1 cwt.

15. Express 6 days 12 hr. as the decimal of a week.

16. Reduce 255 days to the decimal of a year of 365 days.

17. What fraction is 1 lb. of 1 kilogram? (1 kg. = 2·205 lb.)

18. Express 3 tons 3 cwt. 2 qr. as a decimal of a ton.

19. 160·25 tons of coal were bought at 96s. a ton and sold at 101s. a ton. How much was gained on the transaction?

20. A man, a woman and a boy receive for a day's work 50s. Of this the man receives 20s., the woman 16s.; what fraction of the whole does the boy receive?

21. A Swiss 20-franc note is worth £1·614; find the value of 250·15 francs.

22. Add together £3¼, 9 guineas, 6 half-crowns, and express the result as the decimal of £1.

23. Express 5 days 8 hr. 30 min. as the decimal of a day.

24. Find the difference between £2·14 and 2·14 guineas.

25. Add the following and express the result as the decimal of a cwt.: 3·5 tons, 8·15 cwt., 4·23 lb. (Notice that in 3·5 tons the 3 as well as the 0·5 must be multiplied by 20 in order to reduce to cwt.)

CHAPTER TWELVE

WEIGHTS AND MEASURES

WE can weigh or measure things only by referring them to some *standard unit* of weight or measure. Thus we say that one piece of iron is 3 pounds weight, and another 5 pounds weight, referring each piece to the unit "pound". The various units used in British weights and measures are as follows:

Unit of *money*	= a *pound sterling* (£ 1).
Unit of *length*	= a *yard*.
Unit of *surface* (or *area*)	= a *square foot*, that is, a square surface measuring a linear foot each way.
Unit of *solidity* (or *volume*)	= a *cubic foot*, that is, a rectangular solid measuring a linear foot each way.
Unit of *weight*	= a *pound weight*.
Unit of *fluid capacity*	= a *gallon*.
Unit of *time*	= a *day*.

From each of these units we get other units, either by *dividing* the standard unit into a number of equal parts or by *multiplying* it a number of times. The object of doing this is at once apparent when we think of the inconvenience of measuring a large quantity by a small unit, or a small quantity by a large unit. Thus in measuring the distance between London and Edinburgh, it is more convenient to do so in terms of the large measure *mile* than of the small measure yard or foot. And in measuring the distance between one end of a room and the other, it is more convenient to do so in terms of the small measure yard or foot than of any larger measure.

In this way are formed what we know as *tables of weights and measures*. These tables are the bugbear of every British schoolboy, for the simple reason, as you will see, that each standard unit divides or multiplies itself differently from all the others. If each unit were to divide and multiply itself by tens, etc., the same arithmetical operation would do for calculations connected with any of the measures. So long, however, as Britain refuses to adopt the decimal system as used on the Continent, the practical man must be prepared for the task of mastering the principal tables.

Here we shall give one or two examples of how to operate with the tables.

Linear Measure (Length)

British.		Metric.	
12 inches (in.)	= 1 foot (ft.)	10 millimetres (mm.)	= 1 centimetre (cm.)
3 ft.	= 1 yard (yd.)	10 cm.	= 1 decimetre (dm.)
22 yd.	= 1 chain (ch.)	10 dm.	= 1 metre (m.)
10 ch.	= 1 furlong (fur.)	10 m.	= 1 dekametre (Dm.)
8 fur.	= 1 mile.	10 Dm.	= 1 hectometre (Hm.)
		10 Hm.	= 1 kilometre (Km.)

Other units:		Equivalents:	
100 links (lk.)	= 1 ch.	1 in.	= 2·54 cm.
5½ yd.	= 1 pole.	1 m.	= 39·37 in.
6 ft.	= 1 fathom.		= 1·093 6 yd.
3 miles	= 1 league.	1 Km.	= 0·621 4 miles.

The names of the various units in the metric system should be carefully noted. The *metre* is the fundamental unit; all the others are derived from it by the use of the prefixes *centi-*, *deci-*, *kilo-*, etc. These prefixes are also used in conjunction with the other standard units, the gram and the litre. It is necessary to distinguish carefully between *deci-*, meaning one-tenth, and *deka-*, meaning ten times.

In metric measures reduction from one unit to another is accomplished simply by multiplying or dividing by 10 or some power of 10; that is, by shifting the decimal point to the right or left according as we wish to multiply or divide.

Example 1. To reduce 1 mile 57 yd. 2 ft. to inches.

	1 mile
8 fur. = 1 mile	8
	8 fur.
10 ch. = 1 fur.	10
	80 ch.
22 yd. = 1 ch.	22
	160
	160
	1 760 yd.
	57
	1 817 yd
3 ft. = 1 yd.	3
	5 451 ft.
	2
	5 453 ft.
12 in. = 1 ft.	12
	65 436 in.

Note that 1 mile = 1 760 yards.

Example 2. To find the number of miles, etc., in 5 876 402 ft.

$$\begin{array}{r} 3)\overline{5\ 876\ 402} \\ 2)\overline{1\ 958\ 800}\ \text{yd. and 2 ft. over.} \\ \overline{11)979\ 400} \\ \overline{10)89\ 036}\ \text{ch. and 8 yd. over.} \\ \overline{8)8\ 903}\ \text{fur. and 6 ch. over.} \\ \overline{1\ 112}\ \text{miles and 7 fur. over.} \end{array}$$

Thus the answer is 1 112 miles 7 fur. 6 ch. 8 yd. 2 ft. Notice that in dividing by 22 to reduce yards to chains we use the factors 2 and 11.

Example 3. What is the sum in metres of the following quantities: 3 462 centimetres, 854 millimetres, 923 decimetres, 845 centimetres, 5 643 millimetres?

Since a centimetre is 2 places to the right of the metre we divide 3 462 by 10 × 10, or 10^2, which gives 34·62 metres.

Similarly:

$$\begin{aligned} 854\ \text{millimetres} &= 854 \div (10 \times 10 \times 10) \\ &= 0\text{·}854\ \text{metres.} \\ 923\ \text{decimetres} &= 92\text{·}3\ \text{metres.} \\ 845\ \text{centimetres} &= 8\text{·}45\ \text{metres.} \\ 5\ 643\ \text{millimetres} &= 5\text{·}643\ \text{metres.} \end{aligned}$$

$$\begin{array}{r} \text{Hence sum} = 34\text{·}62 \\ 0\text{·}854 \\ 92\text{·}3 \\ 8\text{·}45 \\ 8\text{·}45 \\ 5\text{·}643 \\ \hline 141\text{·}867\ \text{metres.} \end{array}$$

Example 4. How many pieces of string, each 35 cm. long, can be cut off from a piece 75·62 m. long?

$$75 \cdot 62 \text{ m.} = 7\,562 \text{ cm.}$$
$$\therefore \text{ number of pieces} = 7\,562 \div 35$$
$$= 216 \text{ and } 2 \text{ cm. over.}$$

Example 5. To find in miles, chains and yards the length of a railway 94 Km. 415 m. long.

Taking 1 m. as equal to 1·093 6 yd.,
then 94 Km. 415 m. = 94 415 m.

$$= (94\,415 \times 1 \cdot 093\,6) \text{ yd.}$$
$$= \frac{94\,415 \times 1 \cdot 093\,6}{1\,760} \text{ miles}$$
$$= 58 \cdot 668 \text{ miles (nearly).}$$

Now, there are $8 \times 10 = 80$ ch. in 1 mile. Thus:

$$
\begin{array}{r}
0 \cdot 668 \\
80 \\
\hline
53 \cdot 440 \text{ ch.} \\
22 \\
\hline
880 \\
880 \\
\hline
9 \cdot 680 \text{ yd.}
\end{array}
$$

The required length is therefore 58 miles 53 ch. 9 yd.

EXERCISE 19

Reduce:

1. 3 miles 6 fur. 3 ch. 14 yd. 1 ft. 6 in. to inches.
2. 15 miles 1 269 yd. to yards.
3. 6 fur. 3 ch. 21 yd. to feet.
4. 15 miles 15 poles to yards.
5. 3 miles 69 ch. to links.

Express in miles, fur., etc.:

6. 648 732 in.
7. 5 379 ft.
8. 528 000 ft.

   9. 538 yd.
  10. 1 936¼ yd.

Express in metres and add:

  11. 326 cm., 48 056 mm., 4 278 cm.
  12. 560 Dm., 924 dm., 564 381 mm., 9 201 dm.
  13. 58 423 mm., 98 Km., 9 356 cm., 8 456 dm.

Express in kilometres and add:

  14. 8 234 dm., 9 236 m.
  15. 920 Hm., 420 Km., 842 635 mm.
  16. 8 245 cm., 924 Km., 84 365 mm., 2 356 cm., 84 573 mm.
  17. Multiply 3 miles 5 fur. 7 ch. 3 yd. by 8.
  18. Multiply 3 Km. 5 Hm. 7 Dm. 3 m. by 8.
  19. Multiply 8·915 m. by 13.
  20. Divide 17 miles 931 yd. by 6 and also by 19.
  21. Divide 12 345·6 m. by 15.
  22. Divide 176 m. by 610.
  23. How many strips of cloth each measuring 1·5 m. can be cut off a piece measuring 10·75 m.?
  24. How many pieces of fence 4 ft. 3 in. long are needed to go round a square field whose side is 370 yd.?
  25. A certain journey is 4 miles 397 yd., and a motorist does it 22 times a week. How far does he drive in six weeks?
  26. How many pieces of cardboard 3 mm. thick are there in a pile 1·5 m. high?
  27. Express 1 yd. as a decimal of 1 metre.
  28. Express 1 cm. as a decimal of 1 inch.
  29. What is the height in (1) metres, (2) kilometres, of a mountain 14 501 ft. high?
  30. Find the length in miles of a journey of 872 Km.

Square Measure (Area)

British.	Metric.
144 sq. in. = 1 sq. ft.	100 sq. mm. = 1 sq. cm.
9 sq. ft. = 1 sq. yd.	100 sq. cm. = 1 sq. dm.
484 sq. yd. = 1 sq. ch.	100 sq. dm. = 1 sq. m.
10 sq. ch. = 1 acre.	100 sq. m. = 1 sq. Dm.
640 acres = 1 sq. mile	100 sq. Dm. = 1 sq. Hm.
	100 sq. Hm. = 1 sq. Km.

  Other units:

30¼ sq. yd. = 1 sq. pole.	100 sq. m. is called 1 are.
40 sq. poles = 1 rood.	100 ares = 1 hectare.
4 roods = 1 acre.	

  Note that 4 840 sq. yd. = 1 acre.

The unit of Surface is a *square foot*; that is, a square surface measuring 1 foot each way. Now, if one side of this square foot be divided into 12 equal parts, each of these parts will be equal to 1 inch; and if a side adjacent to this side be also divided into 12 equal parts, each of these parts will be equal to 1 inch. Then by drawing straight lines through the first and second sets of divisions we can divide the square foot into 144 smaller squares, each of which will be a *square inch*. Now, there are 12 squares in each row, and there are 12 rows; therefore there are 12 times 12 squares, or 144 squares in all. Similarly, in 1 sq. yd. there will be 3 ft. × 3 ft., or 9 sq. ft.; and in 1 sq. pole there will be $5\frac{1}{2}$ yd. × $5\frac{1}{2}$ yd., or $30\frac{1}{4}$ sq. yd., which = 1 sq. pole. 40 sq. poles make what is called 1 rood, and 4 roods make 1 acre.

The metric unit of surface is the *square metre*. The principal other units used in practice are the *are* and the *hectare*. Manipulations in square measure are almost as simple as they are in linear measure.

The relations between the British and metric units can be derived from those already given in linear measure.

Example 6. Express in square metres and add 3 256 sq. m., 8 426 sq. dm., 181 Dm., 25 sq. cm.

3 256 sq. m.	= 3 256·	sq. m.
8 426 sq. dm.	= 84·26	,,
181 sq. Dm.	= 18 100·	,,
25 sq. cm., or		
0·25 sq. dm.	= 0·002 5	,,
	21 440·262 5	,,

Example 7. Find the number of acres in 1 hectare.

We know that 1 metre = 1·093 6 yd.
Therefore 1 sq. m.   = 1·093 6 × 1·093 6 sq. yd.
                     = 1·196 sq. yd.
Therefore 1 hectare   = 11 960 sq. yd. (approximately)
$$= \frac{11\ 960}{4\ 840} \text{ acres}$$
                     = 2·471 acres.

Cubic Measure (Volume)

British.	Metric.
1 728 cu. in. = 1 cu. ft.	1 000 cu. mm. = 1 cu. cm.
27 cu. ft. = 1 cu. yd.	1 000 cu. cm. = 1 cu. dm.
	and so on through the table.

Cubic measure, or the measure of solidity, is derived from linear measure in a similar way to that in which square measure was derived. A block of wood measuring 1 foot each way can be divided into small blocks, each measuring 1 inch. For, from what we have seen in square measure, one face of the block can be divided into 144 small blocks measuring 1 inch each way; and we can cut off 12 rows of these blocks, or 12 times 144 blocks, that is, 1 728 blocks in all. (The diagram on p. 156 will show the truth of this.) In other words, there will be 12 × 12 × 12, or 1 728 cu. in. in 1 cu. ft. Similarly, there are 3 × 3 × 3, or 27 cu. ft. in 1 cu. yd.

Example 8. Find the relation between 1 cu. yd. and 1 cu. m.

We know that 1 metre = 1·093 6 yd.
Therefore 1 cu. m.   = 1·093 6 × 1·093 6 × 1·093 6
                       cu. yd.
                     = 1·308 cu. yd. (nearly).

EXERCISE 20

1. How many cubic centimetres are there in 2 cu. m.?
2. How many square metres are there in 100 ares?
3. Express in cubic metres and add 91 118·64 cu. dm., 15 cu. dm., and 81 456 cu. cm.
4. What is the difference in cubic metres between 28 567 cu. cm. and 54 263 cu. dm.?
5. Express 1 acre as a decimal of 1 hectare.
6. Express 1 sq. cm. in sq. in.
7. Find the number of cu. mm. in 1 cu. in.

Weight

British (Avoirdupois).	Metric.
16 drams = 1 ounce (oz.)	10 milligrams (mg.) =
16 oz. = 1 pound (lb.)	1 centigram (cg.)
28 lb. = 1 quarter (qr.)	and so on.
4 qr. = 1 hundredweight (cwt.)	
20 cwt. = 1 ton.	1 000 Kg. is called 1 metric tonne.

Also: 14 lb.   = 1 stone
      100 lb. = 1 cental.
     2 240 lb. = 1 ton.

For weighing gold, silver, etc., the table used is called *Troy Weight*:

24 grains (gr.) = 1 pennyweight (dwt.)
20 dwt.   = 1 ounce.

Useful relations:

1 lb.	= 7 000 gr.	1 Kg.	= 2·205 lb.
1 oz. avoir.	= 437½ gr.	1 metric tonne	= 0·984 ton.
1 oz. troy	= 480 gr.		

Capacity

British.	Metric.
4 gills = 1 pint (pt.)	10 centilitres (cl.) =
2 pt. = 1 quart (qt.)	1 decilitre (dl.)
4 qt. = 1 gallon (gall.)	and so on.
2 gall. = 1 peck (pk.)	
4 pk. = 1 bushel (bush.)	
8 bush. = 1 quarter (qr.)	

These units are used for measuring both liquids and solids, the smaller ones as a rule for liquids only, and the larger ones for dry measure. They have therefore a close relationship with the units of volume. Some equivalents are:

1 gall. contains 277·274 cu. in. and = 4·546 litres (l.)
1 cu. ft. contains 6·23 gall.
1 l. contains 61·03 cu. in. and = 1·76 pints.
1 l. contains 1 000 cu. cm.

Money

British.
12 pence (d.) = 1 shilling (s.)
20 shillings = 1 pound (£).

French.	American.
100 centimes = 1 franc.	100 cents = 1 dollar.

The relations between British and foreign units of money fluctuate from day to day.

The methods of using all these tables are exactly the same in essence as those already worked out above. We add one example of a slightly more difficult nature:

Example 9. The rent of a farm of 35 hectares 25 ares is 80 000 Belgian francs. What is the rent per acre in English money, taking 150 francs to equal £1?

$$1 \text{ hectare} = 2 \cdot 47 \text{ acres};$$

so
$$35 \cdot 25 \text{ hectares} = 35 \cdot 25 \times 2 \cdot 47 \text{ acres}$$
$$= 87 \cdot 07 \text{ acres.}$$

Also
$$150 \text{ francs} = £1;$$

so
$$80\,000 \text{ francs} = £\frac{80\,000}{150} = £\frac{1\,600}{3}.$$

Hence 87·07 acres cost £533·3,
and so 1 acre costs £533·3 ÷ 87·07,
$$= £6 \text{ 2s. 6d., very nearly.}$$

Exercise 21

1. Express 37 209 cg. in British units of weight.
2. Find the volume of 1 850 litres in cu. ft.
3. Find the number of cu. cm. contained in 1 pint.
4. A man sold 3 500 sq. m. of land for 90 000 francs. What was the price: (1) per are; (2) per acre?
5. A cask contains 9·35 Hl. of liquid. 650 litres are drawn off; how much is left?
6. A milkman pays 90 francs for 110 litres of milk, which he sells at 2 francs 90 centimes per litre. Find his profit.
7. How many hectolitres are there in 40 gallons 3 pints?
8. If cloth is sold at 3s. 6¼d. per yd., what is the corresponding price in francs and centimes, taking £1 to be equivalent to 980 francs?
Note that the abbreviation gr. stands for grains. Grams are abbreviated to g. or gm.
9. Express 2 tons 11 cwt. 67 lb. in kilograms.
10. 1 cu. cm. of water weighs 1 gm. Find the weight in lb. of 1 cu. ft. of water.
11. Oil weighs 0·9 times as much as water. Find the weight in British units of 238 cl. of oil.
12. The bill for a meal on board ship is 310 francs, but the waiter is prepared to take 6s. 3d. instead. Which is the better offer, if there are 988 francs to the pound?

CHAPTER THIRTEEN

SQUARES, CUBES, SQUARE AND CUBE ROOTS

Square and Square Root

When a number is multiplied by itself the product is called the *square* of the number, or the number is said to be *squared*. Thus $8 \times 8 = 64$, and 64 is the square of 8. 64 is also said to be the *second power* of 8. In the same way 512 is called the cube of 8, or 8 to the *third power*, and so on. Instead of writing the expression 8×8 in full, we write 8^2; similarly, $8 \times 8 \times 8 = 8^3$, and so on. It is very convenient in practical work to remember the squares of the first 25 numbers at least, without going through the multiplication process.

They are as follows:

$1^2 = 1$	$14^2 = 196$
$2^2 = 4$	$15^2 = 225$
$3^2 = 9$	$16^2 = 256$
$4^2 = 16$	$17^2 = 289$
$5^2 = 25$	$18^2 = 324$
$6^2 = 36$	$19^2 = 361$
$7^2 = 49$	$20^2 = 400$
$8^2 = 64$	$21^2 = 441$
$9^2 = 81$	$22^2 = 484$
$10^2 = 100$	$23^2 = 529$
$11^2 = 121$	$24^2 = 576$
$12^2 = 144$	$25^2 = 625$
$13^2 = 169$	

The *cubes*, or even higher powers, of at least the first 12 numbers can be easily calculated mentally.

The converse process of finding what number multiplied by itself will equal a certain number is called finding the *square root*. Thus, in the expression $8 \times 8 = 64$, 64, as we have seen, is called the *square* of 8. Conversely, 8 is called the *square root* of 64. In the same way 8 is called the *cube root* of 512. The symbol for the square root of a number is $\sqrt{}$; thus $\sqrt{49}$ reads the "square root of 49".

The necessity for finding the square root of a number is illustrated by the following problem:

A square field containing 30 acres is to be fenced round. What will be the cost at 6s. per yd. of fencing?

Here we must find the perimeter of the square. But all the sides are of the same length; therefore find the length of one. Now, as the field is square and the area $= l \times b = l \times l = l^2 = (30 \text{ acres}) = 145\,200$ sq. yd., if we can find the number in linear measure which when multiplied by itself will $= 145\,200$ sq. yd., that is, if we can find the square root of 145 200, we shall have the length of the side of the field in yards.

Method of Finding Square Root

First. Some numbers can be factorised, and their square root will be the *product of the square roots of the separate factors*.

Example 1. Find the square root of 2 025.

Since
$$2\,025 = 25 \times 81,$$
$$\therefore \qquad \sqrt{2\,025} = \sqrt{25} \times \sqrt{81}$$
$$= 5 \times 9$$
$$= 45.$$

Example 2. Find $\sqrt{6\,561}$.

$$6\,561 = 9 \times 729$$
$$= 9 \times 9 \times 81$$
$$= 81 \times 81;$$

$$\therefore \qquad \sqrt{6\ 561} = \sqrt{81} \times \sqrt{81}$$
$$= 9 \times 9$$
$$= 81;$$

or *shorter*,

Since $\qquad 6\ 561 = 81^2,$

$\therefore \qquad \sqrt{6\ 561} = 81.$

EXERCISE 22

Find by method of factors the square foot of:

1. 256, 441, 625.
2. 1 225, 1 296, 3 249.
3. 1 444, 7 056, 7 569.
4. 30 625, 16 900, 99 225.

Second. When the number cannot be easily factorised.

Example 3. Find the square root of 746 496.

```
746496(864
64
─────
166)1064
    996
─────
1724)6896
     6896
```

Note: The answer can be placed above 746 496 or after 746 496 (as in this example).

The process is as follows:

1. Mark off periods of *two* figures each, beginning at the unit's place and going *to the left*.

2. Take the first period, viz., 74, and put in the answer the square root of the next square number below 74, which is 64.

3. Subtract the square of 8, i.e., 64 from the period, and take down the next period.

4. Double the part of the answer already found, viz., 8, and place this as a *trial* divisor to 1 064.

5. Find how often this trial divisor goes into 106; place this figure (6) in the answer and *alongside the trial divisor*, and multiply the whole divisor 166 by it. This gives 996.

6. Subtract 996 from 1 064, and put down the next period.

7. Again, as in 4, double the part of the answer already found, which gives 172 as a trial divisor, and so on.

Example 4.
$$7\overline{16}\overline{56}\overline{22}\overline{25}(8465$$
$$64$$
$$\overline{164)765}$$
$$656$$
$$\overline{1686)10962}$$
$$10116$$
$$\overline{16925)84625}$$
$$84625$$

In the case of decimal numbers point as in whole numbers from the unit's place, to left and right.

Example 5. $\sqrt{803\cdot7}$.
$$803\cdot7\overline{00}\overline{00}(28\cdot34 \ldots$$
$$4$$
$$\overline{48)403}$$
$$384$$
$$\overline{563)1970}$$
$$1689$$
$$\overline{5664)28100}$$
$$22656$$
$$\overline{5444}$$

Example 6. $\sqrt{91}$ to two decimal places.

$$
\begin{array}{r}
9\dot{1}\cdot 0\dot{0}0\dot{0}(9\cdot 53 \\
81 \\
\hline
185)1000 \\
925 \\
\hline
1903)7500 \\
5709 \\
\hline
1791
\end{array}
$$

Worked Examples of the Application of Square Root

Example 7. Find the length of the side of a square field containing 11 acres 1 rood 10 sq. poles $3\frac{1}{2}$ sq. yd.

First reduce the given area to sq. yd., thus:

$$
\begin{array}{r}
\text{11 acres 1 rood 10 sq. poles } 3\frac{1}{2} \text{ sq. yd.} \\
4 \\
\hline
45 \\
40 \\
\hline
1\ 810 \\
30\frac{1}{4} \\
\hline
452\frac{1}{2} \\
54\ 303\frac{1}{2} \\
\hline
54\ 756 \text{ sq. yd.}
\end{array}
$$

Hence the length of the side of the square
$= \sqrt{54\ 756}$ sq. yd., or 234 linear yd., found as follows:

$$54756(234$$
$$4$$

$$43)147$$
$$129$$

$$464)1856$$
$$1856$$

Example 8. Find the cost of putting a fence, at 3s. per yard., round a square field whose area is $2\frac{1}{2}$ acres.

$$\text{I acre} = 4\,840 \text{ sq. yd.;}$$
$$\therefore 2\frac{1}{2} \text{ acres} = (9\,680 + 2\,420) \text{ sq. yd.}$$
$$= 12\,100 \text{ sq. yd.}$$

$$\dot{1}\dot{2}\dot{1}\dot{0}\dot{0}(110$$
$$1$$
$$21 \qquad 21$$
$$21$$

$$00$$

Square root of 12 100 sq. yd. is 110 yd.;

$$\therefore \text{ perimeter of field} = 4 \times 110 \text{ yd.}$$
$$= 440 \text{ yd.;}$$
$$\therefore \text{ cost of fencing} = \pounds(440 \times \tfrac{3}{20})$$
$$= \pounds66.$$

EXERCISE 23

Find the length of the side of a square field whose area is:

1. 4 acres.
2. 10 acres 36 sq. poles.
3. 10 000 sq. yd.
4. 7 acres 2 601 sq. yd.

D

5. 2 sq. miles 4 acres 20 sq. poles.

6. A square court contains $\frac{1}{4}$ acre. Find the length of one side in yards correct to three decimal places.

7. The area of a square garden is 4 rd. 1 pl. 29 yd. $6\frac{3}{4}$ ft. Find the length of its side.

8. Find the cost of fencing a square field of $3\frac{1}{2}$ acres in extent, at 5s. per yd.

9. How many yards of barbed wire will be required to fence a square garden whose area is 3 600 sq. yd., the wire to be in three rows?

10. The area of the six faces of a cubical box is 1 830 sq. ft. Find the length of its edge.

11. What breadth of square carpet will be required to cover an area of 1 849·5 sq. ft.?

12. A square field of 12 acres is laid out as a cricket ground. The space reserved for spectators is a strip of uniform breadth all round, 2 acres in area. What is the length of the side of the cricket ground proper?

Cube Root

The method of finding *cube roots* by factors is similar to that for finding square roots, and is illustrated below. There is also a general method for finding cube roots corresponding to the general method for square roots, but it is very laborious and seldom used. In practice it is better to use tables. Most cheap sets of mathematical tables include both square and cube roots, and these are indispensable to anyone who has to perform the process often.

Example 9. $\sqrt[3]{729}$.

$$\text{Since } 729 = 9 \times 81$$
$$= 9 \times 9 \times 9$$
$$= 9^3,$$
$$\therefore \sqrt[3]{729} = 9.$$

Example 10. $\sqrt[3]{85\ 184}$.

$$\text{Since } 85\ 184 = 11 \times 7\ 744$$
$$= 11 \times 11 \times 704$$
$$= 11 \times 11 \times 11 \times 64$$
$$= 11^3 \times 4^3,$$

$$\therefore \sqrt[3]{85\ 184} = 11 \times 4$$
$$= 44$$

EXERCISE 24

Find by the method of factors the cube root of:

1. 216, 1 331, 1 728.
2. 512, 2 197, 2 744.
3. 3 375, 5 832, 4 913.
4. Find the cost of lining the inside of a cubical box (lid included) containing $42\frac{7}{8}$ cu. ft., at 9d. per sq. ft.
5. A rectangular piece of metal measuring 4 ft., 10 ft. and 25 ft. is to be melted down and remoulded into a cube. What must be the length of the edge of the cube?
6. A cubical cistern is 5 ft. deep. What must be the depth of another cubical cistern which is to hold 8 times as much?

CHAPTER FOURTEEN

SIMPLE EQUATIONS AND PROBLEMS

Equations

In every arithmetical problem our object is to find the value of some unknown quantity from the known values of certain other quantities. And all the fundamental operations of addition, subtraction, etc., are of practical use only in so far as they help us to find this unknown quantity. In algebra it is the same. Certain conditions are given us, and the relation between these conditions; and from this information we frame what is called an *equation* or an equality; and, by means of the processes of addition, subtraction, multiplication and division, we find the unknown quantity of which we are in search. For example, in the formula $\frac{1}{2}mv^2 = Fs$ we have given that half of the mass × the square of the velocity = the force × the space through which the force acts. This is an equation or an equality between two quantities. Suppose now that v is the unknown quantity in the above equation, and that $m = 8$, $F = 135$, $s = 10$. Then the equation becomes

$$\frac{1}{2} \times 8 \times v^2 = 135 \times 10,$$
$$\therefore \quad 4v^2 = 1\ 350,$$
$$\therefore \quad v^2 = 337 \cdot 5,$$
$$\therefore \quad v = \sqrt{337 \cdot 5}$$
$$= 18 \cdot 37.$$

In finding the value of the unknown quantity v, or in what is called *solving the equation*, we divided each side of the equation $4v^2 = 1\ 350$ by 4, relying on the self-evident truth that when equal quantities are divided by the same quantity the quotients are equal. Similarly, in the next equation, $v^2 = 3\,375$, we rely on the fact that the square roots of equal quantities are equal.

The axioms, or self-evident truths on which we rely in solving equations, may be summed up as follows:

1. Axiom of Addition. If equal quantities be added to each side of an equation the sums are equal.

2. Axiom of Subtraction. If equal quantities be subtracted from each side of an equation the remainders are equal.

3. Axiom of Multiplication. If each side of an equation be multiplied by equal quantities the products are equal.

4. Axiom of Division. If each side of an equation be divided by equal quantities the quotients are equal.

Also the two sides will still be equal when the square root, cube root, etc., of each side is taken.

These axioms are true of both arithmetical and algebraical quantities.

Let us see how they apply in the following example:

$$3x - 2 = 5x - 7.$$

Here the unknown x appears on both sides of the equation. Known numbers also appear on both sides. But we want the unknown numbers to appear on one side, and the known on the other side, for we want to be able to say that $x =$ some known number. Now, applying the axiom of subtraction, we can get rid of $5x$ on the right-hand side by *subtracting* $5x$ from both sides, which makes the equation:

$$3x - 5x - 2 = 5x - 5x - 7,$$
or $\qquad 3x - 5x - 2 = -7.$

Similarly, to get rid of -2 on the left-hand side we *add* 2 to both sides, which makes the equation:

$$3^x - 5x - 2 + 2 = -7 + 2,$$
or $\qquad$ $3^x - 5x = -7 + 2.$

But a little consideration will show that this process is the same thing as if we were to *transpose* the quantities from one side to the other and *change their sign*. Thus:

$$3^x - 2 = 5x - 7$$
becomes $3^x - 5x = -7 + 2.$

Hence the convenient rule (*which, however, is meaningless apart from the above explanation*): Transpose all the terms containing the unknown quantity to one side, and all the known quantities to the other, *changing the signs of all the transposed terms*.

Example 1.

$$2x - x - 4 + 7 = 3x - 6 + 10,$$
$$2x - x - 3x = -6 + 10 - 7 + 4,$$
$$-2x = +1;$$

∴ (dividing by -2) $x = \dfrac{1}{-2} = -\dfrac{1}{2}.$

Example 2.

$$15(x - 1) + 4(x + 3) = 2(7 + x),$$
∴ $15x - 15 + 4x + 12 = 14 + 2x,$
∴ $15x + 4x - 2x \qquad = 14 - 12 + 15$ (by axioms 1
$\qquad\qquad\qquad\qquad\qquad$ and 2),
∴ $\qquad\qquad 17x \qquad = 17,$
∴ $\qquad\qquad x \qquad = 1 \qquad\qquad$ (by axiom 4).

Example 3. Example of a *fractional* equation:

$$\frac{x + 5}{6} + \frac{x + 1}{9} = \frac{x + 3}{4}.$$

Here we first get rid of the fractional form by multiplying each side by *such a quantity as will cause* 6, 9 *and* 4 *to disappear.* Now, the *multiplier* of each side which will cause 6, 9 and 4 to disappear will be a *common multiple* of 6, 9 and 4. And it will be convenient to get the *lowest* common multiple. This is 36.

Accordingly, when we multiply each side by 36 we get:

$$36\frac{(x+5)}{6} + 36\frac{(x+1)}{9} = 36\frac{(x+3)}{4},$$

or $\qquad 6(x+5) \times 4(x+1) = 9(x+3),$

or $\qquad 6x + 30 + 4x + 4 = 9x + 27,$

$\therefore \qquad 10x - 9x = 27 - 34,$

$$x = -7.$$

EXERCISE 25

Solve the following equations:

1. $2x - 3 = -4x - 9.$
2. $x - 4 = 9 - 2x.$
3. $x^2 - 5 = x^2 - x.$
4. $2x - 3 - 5x = 8 - x.$
5. $p - 6 + 2p = 3 - p.$
6. $\dfrac{x+1}{2} - \dfrac{x-1}{3} = 6.$
7. $\dfrac{5x}{2} + \dfrac{3x}{4} = \dfrac{x}{2} + 1.$
8. $\dfrac{x-1}{3} - \dfrac{x-2}{4} = \dfrac{x-3}{5}.$
9. $\dfrac{2x}{3} + \dfrac{x}{5} - \dfrac{3x}{7} = 18.$
10. $\dfrac{2(x+1)}{7} - \dfrac{3(x+2)}{8} = \dfrac{x}{2}.$
11. $\frac{1}{4}(x+3) - \frac{1}{3}(2x+1) = 3x.$ [*First step:* $3(x+3) - 4(2x+1) = 36x.$]
12. $\frac{2}{3}(x+5) + \frac{3}{4}(x+7) = 3(x-1).$
13. $\dfrac{x}{2} + \dfrac{x}{3} - \dfrac{x}{4} + \dfrac{x}{5} = 14.$
14. $0.5x - \frac{2}{3}x - 0.5 = 4\frac{1}{2}.$ [*First step:* $\frac{1}{2}x - \frac{2}{3}x - \frac{1}{2} = \frac{9}{2}.$]
15. $0.15x - 2x + 0.75 = 0.3 + 2\frac{1}{2} - x.$
16. Find the value of A in the equation $A = \frac{1}{2}hb$, when $h = 12$ and $b = 11$.
17. Find the value of V in the equation $V = \frac{1}{3}a^2h$, when $a = 16$ and $h = 20$.

18. Find the value of s in the equation $s = \frac{1}{2}gt^2$, when $g = 32 \cdot 2$ and $t = 7$.

19. Find the value of s in the equation $\frac{1}{2}mv^2 = Fs$, when $m = 7$, $F = 110$, $v = 8$.

20. Find the value of a in the equation $v^2 - u^2 = 2as$, when $v = 50$, $u = 12$, $s = 100$.

21. In the formula $F = \dfrac{mv^2}{gr}$ find m when $F = 120$, $v = 40$, $g = 32$ and $r = 4$.

22. In the equation $v^2 = 2fs$ find the value of v when $s = 300$ and $f = 2\frac{1}{2}$.

23. In the equation $\dfrac{w}{w - 300} = \dfrac{13}{2}$ find the value of w.

24. In the equation $s = Vt + \frac{1}{2}ft^2$ find the value of V when $s = 120$, $t = 1$, $f = 32$.

25. In the equation of the previous exercise find the value of f when $s = 8\,000$, $V = 20$, and $t = 50$.

26. In the formula $I = \dfrac{PNR}{100}$ find the value of I when $P = 400$, $N = 3$, $R = 2\frac{1}{2}$.

27. In the formula $P = \dfrac{100\,I}{NR}$ find the value of P when $I = 60$, $N = 2$, $R = 3\frac{1}{2}$.

28. In the formula $N = \dfrac{100\,I}{PR}$ find the value of N when $I = £6$ 17s. 6d., $P = £320$, and $R = 2\frac{1}{2}$.

29. In the formula $R = \dfrac{100\,I}{PN}$ find the value of R when $I = £60$, $P = £1\,015$, $N = 2\frac{1}{2}$.

30. In the formula $A = 2h(l + b)$ find the value of
     (1) A when $h = 15$, $l = 25$, $b = 15$;
     (2) h when $A = 405$, $l = 10$, $b = 8$.

Solution of Problems by Equations

Nearly every question in applied science resolves itself into the solution of an equation. Thus, in the case of a body falling vertically from rest, the relation between the space described and the time of falling is expressed in the formula $s = \frac{1}{2}gt^2$, where s denotes the space described, t the time in seconds, and $g = 32 \cdot 2$ ft. per second per second (i.e., the acceleration of a body falling freely). Now, suppose we want to find the depth of a well which we cannot conveniently measure directly.

In the law $s = \frac{1}{2}gt^2$ we can easily find t by dropping a stone to the bottom and counting the time in seconds. Suppose the time is 2 sec. Then

$$s = \frac{1}{2} \times 32 \cdot 2 \times 2^2$$
$$= 16 \cdot 1 \times 4$$
$$= 64 \cdot 4 \text{ ft.}$$

But besides their value in applied science, equations are often of considerable service in solving arithmetical problems that present some difficulty.

Example 4. How much tea at 6s. per lb. must be mixed with 5 lb. of tea at 5s. per lb., so that the mixture may be worth 5s. 6d. per lb.?

Let x = required number of lb. of tea at 6s. per lb.; then, from the statement of the problem, price of x lb. + price of 5 lb. = price of $(x + 5)$ lb.

But price of x lb. $= 6x$ shillings,
„ 5 lb. $= 25$ shillings,
„ $(x + 5)$ lb. $= \{5\frac{1}{2} \times (x + 5)\}$ shillings;
$$\therefore \quad 6x + 25 = \frac{11(x + 5)}{2};$$

multiplying each side by 2,
$$\therefore \quad 12x + 50 = 11x + 55;$$
$$\therefore \qquad\qquad x = 5.$$
$\therefore$ 5 lb. of tea at 6s. per lb. must be taken.

Example 5. A merchant mixes 52 gall. of spirit at 15s. 9d. per gallon with 60 gall at 16s. 11d. At what price per gallon must he sell the mixture so as to gain 10%?

Let x = price per gallon in shillings. Then, from the statement:

$$52 \times 15/9 + 60 \times 16/11 = 112x - \tfrac{1}{10} \text{ of total cost of}$$
$$\text{mixture.}$$

$$52 \times 15\tfrac{3}{4} + 60 \times 16\tfrac{11}{12}$$

$$= \left(\overset{13}{\underset{}{52}} \times \frac{63}{4} \right) + \left(\overset{5}{\underset{}{60}} \times \frac{203}{12} \right) = 819 + 1\,015;$$

$$\therefore\ 819 + 1\,015 = 112x - \tfrac{1}{10}(819 + 1\,015),$$

$$\therefore\ 1\,834 \qquad\quad = 112x - 183 \cdot 4;$$

$$\therefore\ -112x \qquad\ = -1\,834 - 183 \cdot 4,$$

$$\therefore\ 112x \qquad\quad = 2\,017 \cdot 4,$$

$$\therefore\ x \qquad\qquad = 18 \text{ nearly,}$$

$$\therefore\ \text{selling price per gallon is about } 18s.$$

The chief difficulty the beginner in algebra has with equations is not the mere solution, but the *forming of the equation (or equations) from the given conditions*. And this difficulty often arises from the difficulty of expressing the conditions in symbols. Thus, if a man walks 40 miles at the rate of 4 miles an hour, it is easy to tell the time he takes. But when the same sort of problem is expressed in symbolical language—"If a man walks a miles at the rate of b miles per hour, how many hours does he take?"—it is not quite so familiar. Yet, until the student can do this sort of thing quite readily, he is handicapped in all equational work involving problems. Further, an intelligent knowledge of the various formulae of practical science depends on the proper understanding of symbolical expressions, for all formulae are symbolical.

The following are examples of what the student should be able to do in the way of making symbolical expressions:

Example 6. If $T =$ time in hours,

$D =$ distance in miles,

$R =$ rate in miles per hour.

To express each in terms of the others:

$$T = \frac{D}{R}, \quad D = TR, \quad R = \frac{D}{T}.$$

Example 7. If a man walks y miles in x days, what is his rate per day?

$$R = \frac{D}{T}$$
$$= \frac{y}{x}.$$

Example 8. What is the velocity in feet per second of a train which travels 95 miles in x hours?

$$R = \frac{D}{T}$$
$$= \frac{95}{x} \text{ miles per hour,}$$
$$= \left(\frac{95}{x} \div 3\,600 \right) \text{ miles per second,}$$
$$= \frac{95}{3\,600x} \text{ miles per second,}$$
$$= \frac{19}{720x} \text{ miles per second,}$$
$$= \left(\frac{19}{720x} \times 1\,760 \times 3 \right) \text{ ft. per second,}$$
$$= \frac{418}{3x} \text{ ft. per second.}$$

Example 9. If I spend x shillings a week, how many pounds do I save out of a yearly income of £y?

Money spent in a year $= 52x$ shillings
$$= \frac{52x}{20} \text{ pounds,}$$
$$\therefore \text{ money saved} = £\left(y - \frac{13x}{5} \right).$$

Example 10. How long will it take a person to walk p miles if he walks 30 miles in q hours?

$$\text{Rate} = \frac{30}{q}$$

$$\text{and} \quad T = \frac{D}{R}$$

$$= \frac{p}{\frac{30}{q}} = \frac{pq}{30}.$$

EXERCISE 26

1. If the sum of two numbers be 72, and one of them be p, what is the other?

2. If the sum of two numbers be p, and one of them is q, what is the other number?

3. How many hours will it take to walk p miles at $3\frac{1}{2}$ miles an hour?

4. A train goes x miles an hour; how long will it take to go 350 miles?

5. A man has p half-crowns and q florins; how many shillings has he?

6. Find the value in pence of x pounds y shillings and z pence.

7. How long will it take to fill a tank which holds b cu. ft. if it fills at the rate of c cu ft. per hour?

8. If a man walks k miles in q hours, what is his rate of walking?

9. What is the price in shillings of 240 apples when the cost of a score is p pence?

10. What is the distance between two places if a train travelling p miles an hour takes 6 hours to do the journey?

EXERCISE 27

1. Divide a line 16 in. long into two parts such that the length of one is 3 times the length of the other.

2. Divide £1000 between two men so that one may get 5 times as much as the other.

3. A post has $\frac{1}{4}$ of its length in the mud, $\frac{1}{3}$ in the water and 12 ft. of it visible above water. What is the total length of the post?

4. A sum of £8 17s. is made up of 124 coins, some of which are florins and the rest shillings; how many shillings are there and how many florins? (This is an equation in which the equality is

between value and value: thus—value of florins + value of shillings = £8 17s.)

5. Divide £350 between A, B and C so that B and C may each get ⅓ of what A gets.

6. How much tea at 5s. per lb. must be mixed with 20 lb. at 4s. per lb. so as to make the mixture worth 4s. 4d. per lb.?

7. Divide £60 between A, B and C so that A may have £6 more than B, and B £5 more than C.

8. A friend, walking at the rate of 3 miles an hour, starts 2 hours before me. When should I be able to overtake him walking at the rate of 4 miles an hour?

(*Note.* The friend walks $(2 + x)$ hours; and since the *distance* travelled by both will be the same, the equation will be friend's time × rate = my time × rate; for time × rate = distance.)

CHAPTER FIFTEEN

SIMULTANEOUS EQUATIONS

THE meaning and utility of a pair of simultaneous equations may be explained as follows:

In connection with mechanical appliances certain things are found to vary with one another. As one thing increases another may decrease. Thus, the pressure and volume of a given quantity of gas vary in such a way that the greater the pressure becomes, the less the volume becomes. In the case of a machine two forces may be operative, one called the *effort* (E) and the other the *resistance* (R), and it is found that these two forces vary. Now, by experiments it is found out how these forces vary, and the knowledge thus gained is called the *Law of the Machine*. Such laws are of practical value in determining such problems as the kind of machine necessary to do a certain amount of work—it may be lifting some weight. Now, suppose the law of a machine is expressed in the *formula*—

$$E = aR + b,$$

where a and b are constants, and it is found that when E is 16, R is 6; and when E is 40, R is 12. How are we to make the formula give us a *numerical* result which will be of *practical guidance* in the making of the machine?

If we take the first values of E and R the formula becomes—

$$16 = 6a + b.$$

If we take the second values of E and R the formula becomes—

$$40 = 12a + b.$$

Here, then, from two equations we have to find the values of two unknowns—a and b. We proceed as follows:

$$(1) \quad 6a + b = 16.$$
$$(2) \quad 12a + b = 40.$$

Multiply (1) by 2 and we get (according to the axiom)—

$$(3) \quad 12a + 2b = 32.$$

Now subtract (3) from (2) and we get—

$$-b = 8,$$
$$\text{or} \quad b = -8.$$

Substitute the value of b in equation (1) and we get—

$$6a - 8 = 16;$$
$$\therefore \quad 6a = 24,$$
$$\therefore \quad a = 4.$$
$$\text{Now} \quad E = aR + b,$$
$$\therefore \quad E = 4R - 8.$$

This result shows what must be the relation between the *effort* of the machine and the *resistance* it has to overcome.

From the fact that two (or more) equations are given in connection with the *same* problem, the equations are called *simultaneous*; and their solution is found by adding, subtracting, multiplying or dividing in accordance with the axioms given above.

We add other examples of how to solve simultaneous equations.

Example 1. $(1) \quad 2p + q = 50.$
$\qquad\qquad\quad (2) \quad 7p - 3q = 14.$

Multiply (1) by 3 and it becomes—

$$(3)\ 6p + 3q = 150.$$

Add (3) and (2) and we get—

$$(4)\ 13p = 164,$$
$$\therefore\quad p = 12\tfrac{8}{13}.$$

Substitute the value of p in (1) thus:

$$25\tfrac{3}{13} + q = 50.$$
$$\therefore\quad q = 50 - 25\tfrac{3}{13}$$
$$= 24\tfrac{10}{13}.$$

Example 2. If, when A is 3, B is 1, and when A is 8, B is 6, find the values of a and b in the equation $A = aB + b$.

From what is given, we get the following simultaneous equations:

$$(1)\ 3 = a + b.$$
$$(2)\ 8 = 6a + b.$$

Subtracting (2) from (1) we get—

$$-5 = -5a,$$
$$\text{or} - 5a = -5,$$
$$\therefore\quad a = 1.$$

Substituting the value of a in (1) we get—

$$3 = 1 + b,$$
$$\therefore b = 2.$$

Example 3. A grocer wishes to mix tea at 5s. per lb. with another sort at 6s. per lb., so as to make 60 lb. to be sold at 5s. 4d. per lb.; what quantity of each sort must he take?

Let x = number of lb. at 5s.,
and y =   „   „   6s.

Then value of x lb. = $5x$ shillings.
    „   „ y lb. = $6y$ shillings.

Then from the given conditions—

(1) x lb. $+ y$ lb. = 60 lb.
(2) $5x$ shillings $+ 6y$ shillings $= (60 \times 5\frac{1}{3})$ shillings.

Or, to put the equations in a simpler form:

$$\text{(1)} \quad x + y = 60.$$
$$\text{(2)} \quad 5x \times 6y = 320.$$

Multiply (1) by 5 and it becomes—

$$\text{(3)} \quad 5x + 5y = 300.$$

Subtracting (3) from (2) we get $y = 20$.
Substituting the value of y in (1) we get—

$$x + 20 = 60,$$
$$\therefore \qquad x = 40.$$

Ans. 40 lb. at 5s., and 20 lb. at 6s.

(*Verification*—40 × 5s. = 200s.;
        20 × 6s. = 120s.;
    $\therefore$ 60 lb. sell for 320s.,
    $\therefore$ 1 lb. sells for $\frac{32}{6}$s., or 5s. 4d.)

Example 4. Solve the equations:

$$\text{(1)} \quad 3x + 4y = 11.$$
$$\text{(2)} \quad 2x + 3y = 8.$$

It will be seen from the preceding examples that our aim in multiplying either or both equations by some number is to get two equations in which the coefficients of x will be the same, or in which the coefficients of y will be the same. Suppose that we wish to get from the given equations two new equations in which the co-efficients of y will be the same, we shall clearly get two such equations if we multiply both sides of (1) by 3 and both sides of (2) by 4.

$$(1) \text{ gives } 9x + 12y = 33.$$
$$(2) \text{ gives } 8x + 12y = 32.$$
$$\therefore \text{ by subtraction we get } x = 1.$$

If we now substitute this value of x in (1) we get $y = 2$.

If we had wished to get two equations in which the co-efficients of x were the same we should have multiplied both sides of (1) by 2, and both sides of (2) by 3.

Exercise 28

Solve the following equations:

1. $x + y = 4.$
   $x - y = 2.$
2. $3x - y = 4.$
   $x + 2y = 6.$
3. $p - q = 2.$
   $2p - q = -3.$
4. $8x - y = 34.$
   $x + 8y = 53.$
5. $3x = 7y.$
   $12y - 5x = -1.$
6. $2A + B = 3.$
   $3B - A = 7.$
7. $B - A = 6.$
   $-3B - 2A = 9.$
8. If when $F = 100$, $B = 8$, and when F is 210, $B = 16$, find the value of F in the formula $F = aB + c$.
9. Half the sum of two numbers is 20, and three times their difference is 18; find the numbers.
10. 5 lb. of tea and 4 lb. of sugar cost 16s. 2d., and 8 lb. of tea and 6 lb. of sugar cost 25s. 9d.; find the cost of a lb. of each.
11. The wages of 10 men and 6 boys amount to £15. If 4 men together receive £2 more than 4 boys, what are the wages of a man and a boy?

12. If when E is 9, R is 24, and when E is 13, R is 37, find the values of a and b in the equation $E = aR + b$.

13. If when E is 72, W is 168, and when E is $90\frac{1}{2}$, W is 220, what are the values of a and b in the equation $E = aW + b$?

NOTE

We have now given the reader an account of the basic ideas and the simplest uses of algebra. For those who wish to pursue the subject further *Teach Yourself Algebra*, a companion volume to the present one, will be found most suitable.

CHAPTER SIXTEEN

RATIO—PROPORTION—UNITARY METHOD

Ratio

Numbers may be related to one another in various ways. That relation in which we think of the number of times the one number is contained in the other is called a *Ratio*. All fractions may be looked upon as ratios, and the placing of the numerator over the denominator as implying division. Thus, $\frac{1}{2} = 1 \div 2$ where 2 is contained in 1 half a time; $\frac{6}{3} = 2$ where 3 is contained in 6 twice, and so on. The idea of a ratio is the basis of all proportion, and the student must thoroughly understand it.

First, then, we can speak of the ratio between 12 and 3, but we cannot speak of the ratio between 12 sheep and 3 cows. The quantities compared must be *of the same kind* if the ratio is to have any meaning; for it is absurd to say that 3 cows are contained in 12 sheep 4 times. But supposing we know the value of the 12 sheep to be £90, and the value of the 3 cows to be £75, then $\frac{90}{75}$ or $\frac{6}{5}$ has a definite meaning, viz., that the *value* of the three cows is contained in the value of the 12 sheep $\frac{6}{5}$ or $1\frac{1}{5}$ times. Or, to put it in another way, the value of the 12 sheep is $\frac{6}{5}$ or $1\frac{1}{5}$ times the value of the 3 cows; and this leads us to perhaps the simplest definition of *Ratio* as *the number* (whole or fractional) *of times which one quantity is contained in another quantity of the same kind.*

Example 1. The ratio between 2d. and 2s. 6d.

$$= \frac{2d.}{30d.} = \tfrac{1}{15}.$$

Example 2. The ratio between 3 ft. and 10 yd.

$$= \frac{3 \text{ ft.}}{30 \text{ ft.}} = \frac{1}{10}.$$

Example 3. The ratio of 1 oz. avoir. to 1 oz. troy

$$= \frac{437\frac{1}{2} \text{ gr.}}{480 \quad \text{gr.}}$$

$$= \frac{\frac{875}{2}}{480}$$

$$= \frac{875}{960} = \frac{175}{192},$$

that is, 1 oz. avoir. is $\frac{175}{192}$ of 1 oz. troy.

Example 4. The ratio of 4 tons 2 cwt. 3 qr. to 12 cwt.

$$= \frac{4 \text{ tons 2 cwt. 3 qr.}}{12 \text{ cwt.}}$$

$$= \frac{82\frac{3}{4} \text{ cwt.}}{12 \quad \text{cwt.}}$$

$$= \frac{331}{4} \times \frac{1}{12} = \frac{331}{48} = 6\frac{43}{48}.$$

It will be readily seen that this finding of the ratio between two quantities is just the same thing as reducing the one quantity to the fraction of the other, or finding what fraction the one quantity is of the other.

EXERCISE 29

Find the ratios of:
1. 10s. to half a guinea.
2. £5 0s. 6d. to £12 0s. 6d.
3. 18 cwt. 3 qr. 14 lb. to 5 cwt.
4. 73 days to 1 year.
5. 144 sq. miles to 1 acre.
6. 9 sq. yd. to 1 rood.
7. 6 dwt. of gold to 1 lb. of gold.
8. 1 440 yd. to 3½ miles.
9. 7½ miles to 7½ yd.

Which is the larger of the following ratios:

10. $\dfrac{2 \text{ cwt.}}{5 \text{ tons}}$ or $\dfrac{2 \text{ lb.}}{5 \text{ lb.}}$

11. $\dfrac{£7 \text{ 14s.}}{£8 \text{ 6s.}}$ or $\dfrac{£5 \text{ 10s.}}{£6 \text{ 19s.}}$

12. $\dfrac{6\frac{1}{2} \text{ days}}{14 \text{ days}}$ or $\dfrac{3 \text{ weeks}}{7 \text{ weeks}}$.

13. A piece of land measuring 1 acre is to be converted into a garden. Three-fourths of the area is to consist of garden, the rest of walks. What is the ratio of the walk area to that of the garden?

14. A man and a boy are paid £2 for a day's work. Of this sum the man gets £1 7s. In what ratio has the sum been divided?

15. If the diameter of a hoop is $1\frac{1}{2}$ ft. the circumference will be found to be nearly $4\frac{5}{7}$ ft. What is the ratio of the circumference to the diameter?

16. Two trains run a distance of 400 miles in $8\frac{1}{2}$ and 10 hr. respectively. What is the ratio of the two speeds?

17. Find the ratio of the income tax to the total income in each of Nos. 10–13 in Exercise 13.

Proportion

The ratio of 2 to 4 $= \dfrac{2}{4} = \dfrac{1}{2}$; and because these two ratios $\dfrac{2}{4}$ and $\dfrac{1}{2}$ are equal, we say that the numbers 2, 4, 1 and 2 are *in proportion*. In other words, (1) *proportion is the equality of ratios*, or (2) four numbers are in proportion when the ratio of the first to the second equals the ratio of the third to the fourth. Examples: The ratios $\dfrac{12}{6}$, $\dfrac{4}{2}$ are equal, each being equal to 2; and therefore the numbers 12, 6, 4, 2 are in proportion.

Modes of expressing the above and any proportion are as follows:

(1) 12 is to 6 as 4 is to 2.

(2) $\qquad$ 12 : 6 : : 4 : 2.

(3) $\qquad$ $\dfrac{12}{6} = \dfrac{4}{2}$.

In practice the problem connected with proportion is to find one of these four quantities (usually the fourth), having given the other three. The rule for finding this unknown quantity is known as the *Rule of Three*, or Simple Proportion; and its reason or proof may be understood from the following:

Let a, b, c, d represent any four quantities *in proportion* so that $\frac{a}{b} = \frac{c}{d}$. Now, we have already seen that a fraction is unaltered in value if its numerator and denominator are each multiplied or divided by the same number. Multiply then $\frac{a}{b}$ by $\frac{d}{d}$, which gives us $\frac{a \times d}{b \times d}$, and $\frac{c}{d}$ by $\frac{b}{b}$, which gives us $\frac{c \times b}{d \times b}$. The two fractions $\frac{a}{b}$, $\frac{c}{d}$ have thus become changed into the forms $\frac{a \times d}{b \times d}$, $\frac{c \times b}{d \times b}$. Now, since these two *equal* fractions have equal denominators (viz., $b \times d$), their numerators must also be equal. Hence $a \times d = c \times b$, that is, *the product of the first and last terms = the product of the second and third*, or the product of the extreme terms = the product of the mean terms.

But a, b, c, d, stand for any numbers; therefore the statement holds good for any numbers that are in proportion.

From this fact follows a *rule* for finding the fourth or any other term. For since

$$a \times d = b \times c,$$
$$\therefore d = (b \times c) \div a$$
$$= \frac{b \times c}{a}.$$

Or, put in words: the fourth term (d) = the product of the second (b) and third (c) terms divided by the first (a).

That is, put in the ordinary way, *Rule of Three* is, multiply the second and third terms together and divide by the first.

To find the other terms:

1.   Since $a \times d = b \times c$,

$$\therefore \quad a \quad = \frac{b \times c}{d}.$$

2.   Since $a \times d = b \times c$,

$$\therefore \quad b \quad = \frac{a \times d}{c}.$$

3.   Since $a \times d = b \times c$,

$$\therefore \quad c \quad = \frac{a \times d}{b}.$$

Find the unknown term in the following:

Example 5. $x : 8 : : 12 : 16$,

$$\text{that is } \frac{x}{8} = \frac{12}{16},$$

$$\therefore \quad x \times 16 = 8 \times 12,$$

$$\therefore \quad x = \frac{96}{16} = 6.$$

Example 6. $\frac{7}{x} = \frac{19}{114}$,

$$\therefore \quad 7 \times 114 = x \times 19,$$

$$\text{or } x \times \quad 19 = 7 \times 114,$$

$$\therefore \quad x = \frac{7 \times 114}{19}$$

$$= 42.$$

Example 7. $\frac{13}{52} = \frac{x}{56}$,

$$\therefore \quad x \times 52 = 13 \times 56,$$

$$\therefore \qquad x = \frac{\overset{14}{13 \times 56}}{\underset{4}{52}}$$

$$= 14.$$

Example 8. $\qquad \dfrac{18}{14} = \dfrac{72}{x},$

$$\therefore \quad x \times 18 = 14 \times 72,$$

$$\therefore \qquad x = \frac{\overset{4}{14 \times 72}}{\underset{}{18}}$$

$$= 56.$$

When *three* numbers are so related to one another that the first is to the second as the second is to the third, the *second* number is called a *mean proportional* between the other two. Thus the numbers 3, 9, 27 are so related that $3 : 9 : : 9 : 27$; here then 9 is a *mean proportional* to 3 and 27.

Looking back to our letters a, b, c, d, we must represent a mean proportional thus, $\dfrac{a}{b} = \dfrac{b}{c}$.

Here $\qquad\qquad b \times b = a \times c,$

or $\qquad\qquad b^2 \quad = a \times c;$

$\therefore \qquad\qquad b \quad = \sqrt{a \times c}.$

(See under Square Root for further explanation.)

Hence the mean proportional between two numbers = the square root of the product of the two numbers.

Example 9. To find a mean proportional between 18 and 32.

Here the mean proportional $= \sqrt{18 \times 32}$

$$= \sqrt{576}$$

$$= 24.$$

Proof. $\frac{18}{24}$ or $\frac{3}{4} = \frac{24}{32}$ or $\frac{3}{4}$.

EXERCISE 30

Find a fourth proportional to the following numbers:

1. 2, 3, 7.
2. 8, 4, 32.
3. 9, 15, 27.
4. 18, 72, 108.
5. $2\frac{1}{2}$, 3, $17\frac{1}{2}$.

Find the unknown term in the following:

6. $\dfrac{8}{16} = \dfrac{x}{36}$.

7. $\dfrac{3}{1\frac{1}{2}} = \dfrac{x}{16}$.

8. $\dfrac{2}{9} = \dfrac{x}{45}$.

9. $\dfrac{\frac{1}{2}}{\frac{1}{2}} = \dfrac{x}{16}$.

10. $\dfrac{\frac{3}{4}}{\frac{1}{4}} = \dfrac{x}{8}$.

11. $\dfrac{5}{x} = \dfrac{6}{8}$.

12. $\dfrac{1}{x} = \dfrac{8}{13}$.

13. $\dfrac{\frac{1}{2}}{x} = \dfrac{3}{9}$.

14. $\dfrac{7}{x} = \dfrac{56}{72}$.

15. $\dfrac{\frac{1}{4}}{x} = \dfrac{\frac{3}{4}}{8}$.

16. $\dfrac{2}{8} = \dfrac{8}{x}$.

17. $\dfrac{9}{7} = \dfrac{7}{x}$.

18. $\dfrac{3}{21} = \dfrac{21}{x}$.

19. $\dfrac{\frac{1}{2}}{\frac{1}{4}} = \dfrac{\frac{1}{4}}{x}$.

20. $\dfrac{\frac{1}{3}}{9} = \dfrac{9}{x}$.

Find a mean proportional to the following:

21. 2 and 18.
22. 3 and 27.
23. 4 and 16.
24. 5 and 45.
25. $\frac{1}{4}$ and $\frac{1}{9}$.
26. $\frac{1}{2}$ and $\frac{1}{8}$.
27. 3 and 48.
28. 4 and 49.
29. 1 and 9.
30. $\frac{1}{2}$ and $\frac{1}{72}$.

Practical Applications of Ratio and Proportion

Example 10. If it takes 12 men to do a piece of work in 5 days, how many men must be put to do a similar piece of work in 2 days?

Here there are 3 terms given, viz., 5 days, 2 days, 12 men; and the question is how to arrange these *so as to state the right proportion among them and the unknown term*. In the first place, one of the ratios must be either 5 days : 2 days, or 2 days : 5 days; and the other ratio must be either 12 men : required number of men, or required number of men : 12 men. If we take the proportion $\frac{5}{2} = \frac{12}{x}$, we see that since the second term 2 is smaller than the first term 5, *so* the fourth term x must be smaller than the third term 12. But, on the supposition that the working power of the men is all the same, it cannot be that a smaller number of men will do the work of a larger in less time. Hence in stating the proportion we have always to consider whether the unknown fourth term is to be greater or less than the third term. If it is to be greater, then the second term must be greater than the first; if it is to be less, then the second term must be less than the first. In the example, then, a *greater* number of men are wanted to do the work in 2 days; therefore the proportion will be—

$$\text{less} : \text{greater} : : \text{less} : \text{greater},$$
$$\text{that is, } \frac{2}{5} = \frac{12}{x};$$

$$\text{therefore required number of men} = \frac{5 \times \overset{6}{12}}{2}$$
$$= 30.$$

Example 11. If 10 tons 2½ cwt. of sugar are sold for £520 10s., what is the price per lb.?

Here the required fourth term is money, corresponding to £520 10s.; and as the price varies in *direct* proportion to the amount, the fourth term will be less than the third. Hence the proportion will be—

10 tons 2½ cwt. : 1 lb. : : £520 10s. : price per lb.,
$$\text{that is, price per lb.} = \frac{£520 \text{ 10s.} \times 1 \text{ lb.}}{10 \text{ tons } 2\frac{1}{2} \text{ cwt.}}.$$

(1) Notice that £520 10s. is really to be multiplied by the fraction $\dfrac{1 \text{ lb.}}{10 \text{ tons } 2\frac{1}{2} \text{ cwt.}}$.

(2) Keep the quantities in fraction form, and in their highest denominations as much as possible. This saves working with large numbers.

(3) In the present case, you can easily see that the price will be so many pence. But the fraction as it stands is in the form of pounds, shillings; therefore, multiply it by 240.

Proceed thus:

$$\text{Price per lb.} = \frac{£520\frac{1}{2} \times 1 \text{ lb.}}{10 \text{ tons } 2\frac{1}{2} \text{ cwt.}}$$

$$= \frac{\frac{1041}{2} \times \frac{240}{1} \times \frac{1}{112} \text{ cwt.}}{202\frac{1}{2} \text{ cwt.}} \text{ pence}$$

$$= \frac{\overset{347}{\cancel{1041}}}{2} \times \overset{\overset{3}{48}}{\cancel{240}} \times \frac{1}{\underset{7}{\cancel{112}}} \times \frac{\overset{2}{\cancel{2}}}{\underset{\underset{\underset{9}{81}}{27}}{\cancel{405}}} \text{ pence}$$

$$= \frac{347}{63} \text{ pence}$$

$$= 5\frac{32}{63} \text{ pence}$$

$$= 5\frac{1}{2}\text{d. (practically).}$$

N.B. The above method is the shortest that can be adopted *under the Rule of Three*, and the example is worked under that rule simply *as an example of the rule*. The problem might have been solved by simply dividing the total amount of money equally among the total number of pounds, and without any reference to proportion, as follows:

$$10 \text{ tons } 2\frac{1}{2} \text{ cwt.} = 202\frac{1}{2} \text{ cwt.} = (202\frac{1}{2} \times 112) \text{ lb.};$$
$$£520 \text{ 10s.} = \left(\frac{1041}{2} \times 240\right) \text{ pence};$$
$$\therefore \text{ price per lb.} = \frac{\frac{1041}{2} \times 240}{202\frac{1}{2} \times 112} \text{ pence,}$$

which is identical with the Rule of Three result.

Example 12. If £1 is worth 147⅛ Belgian francs, what is the value in English money of a 100-franc note?

Here the fourth term is English money, and it is clearly less than the third term, £1.

Hence
$$\frac{147\frac{1}{8} \text{ fr.}}{100 \text{ fr.}} = \frac{£1}{£x};$$

$$\therefore \text{ value of note} = £x = £\frac{100}{147\frac{1}{8}},$$

$$= \frac{100 \times 240 \times 8}{1\,177} \text{ pence},$$

$$= 163 \text{ pence (nearly)},$$

$$= 13s. \ 7d.$$

EXERCISE 31

1. The weight of 160 ft. of wire rope is 13 cwt. 1 qr. What is the weight of 11 ft.?

2. If 25 men earn £60 12s. 6d. in a given time, how much will 17 men earn in the same time?

3. A housekeeper always spends the same proportion of her allowance on food. In one year she spends £56 5s. on food out of her allowance of £90. The next year she spends £52 10s. on food; what is her allowance then?

4. If 1 metre of cloth costs 3s. 6d., what is the price of 1 yd.? (Take 1 m. = 39⅜ in.)

5. 1 cu. ft. of lead weighs 771 lb. Find the volume of 6 tons of lead.

6. The shadows cast by two objects at the same time are proportional to their heights. If the shadow of a man 5 ft. 10 in. tall is 3 ft. 1 in. long, and the shadow of a wireless pole is 33 ft. long, find the height of the pole.

7. A faulty balance makes 2 lb. appear to weigh 2 lb. 1 oz. What is the true weight when the reading is 7 lb. 4 oz.?

8. A debtor's assets are £609 10s. and his liabilities £2 714 5s. How much can he pay in the pound?

9. A certain salary is £525 a year. What amount should be received between March 1st and June 11th inclusive?

10. A man can do a piece of work in 99 days, working 8 hours a day. How many days would 3 men take, working 7 hours 20 minutes a day?

The Unitary Method

All questions involving the idea of proportion can be solved by what is called the *Unitary Method*. This method deserves considerable attention. The following examples will explain:

Example 13. If 6 lb. of tea cost 27s., what will be the cost of 8 lb.?

$$\begin{aligned}
\text{Cost of 6 lb. of tea} &= 27\text{s.} \\
\therefore \quad \text{,,} \quad \text{1 lb.} \quad \text{,,} &= \tfrac{1}{6} \text{ of 27s.} \\
\therefore \quad \text{,,} \quad \text{8 lb.} \quad \text{,,} &= 8 \times \tfrac{1}{6} \times 27\text{s.} \\
&= 36\text{s.}
\end{aligned}$$

The reasoning is as follows: If 6 lb. of tea cost 27s., 1 lb. will cost *one-sixth* of the cost of 6 lb.; and if 1 lb. cost so much, then 8 lb. will cost 8 times as much. The method gets its name from the fact that from the *unit* of a given quantity we find some other unknown quantity. Thus, in the above example, from the unit price of 1 lb., we find the price of 6 lb.

Example 14. What is the value of 50 qr. of wheat at the rate of 60s. for 5 bush.?

$$\begin{aligned}
\text{Cost of} \quad 5 \text{ bush.} &= 60\text{s.}; \\
\therefore \quad \text{,,} \quad 1 \quad \text{,,} &= \tfrac{1}{5} \text{ of 60s.}; \\
\therefore \quad \text{,,} \quad (50 \times 8) \quad \text{,,} &= \overset{10}{5\!0} \times 8 \times \tfrac{1}{5} \times 60\text{s.} \\
&= 4\,800\text{s.} \\
&= \pounds240.
\end{aligned}$$

Example 15. If from a sack of flour a baker can make 50 loaves weighing 3 lb. each, how many 4 lb. loaves can he make from the same?

By making 3 lb. loaves,

he can make out of the sack   50 loaves;

∴ by making 1 lb. loaves,

he can make out of the sack 3×50;

∴ by making 4 lb. loaves,

he can make out of the sack $\frac{1}{4} \times 3 \times 50$

$$= \frac{150}{4},$$

$$= 37\frac{1}{2} \text{ loaves.}$$

N.B. In arranging the statements of any problem in proportion the quantities that are of the same kind as the answer must come *last*.

If you consider the last fraction brought out by the Unitary Method, it will be found to be exactly the same as that which is produced by the Rule of Three. Which method then is to be adopted? Rule of Three, Unitary Method, or a method depending on first principles alone? The reader must decide the point for himself. He will find, however, that the Unitary Method, though a little longer than the Rule of Three, is more likely to produce the right answer without waste of time. If, therefore, he experiences much trouble in dealing with this type of problem, he would do well always to use the Unitary Method.

EXERCISE 32

1. If 6 cwt. of apples cost £4 15s., what will 35 cwt. cost?

2. If the half-yearly rates on a rental of £50 are £15 6s. 8d., what are they on a rental of £36?

3. A bankrupt's assets are £750 and his liabilities £2 000; what will a creditor who is owed £32 actually receive?

4. If it requires 50½ yd. of carpet ¾ yd. wide to cover a room, how many yd. of carpet ⅝ yd. wide will be necessary to cover the same room?

5. If a garrison of 5 000 men has provisions for 50 days, how long can it last out if it is increased by 100 men?

6. A wages bill at 2s. 2d. an hour is £133 18s.; what would it be if half the work hours were paid at 2s. 8d. instead of 2s. 2d.?

7. In a two-mile race between A and B, A wins by 100 yd.; what handicap can A afford to give B in a race of 1¾ miles?

8. If the cost-of-living index-number is 117 one year, and 122 the next year, find how much more a housekeeper needs in the second year if she spent £73 11s. in the first. (Assume that the index-numbers represent her expenses accurately.)

9. A unit of electricity costs ¾d. How much will it cost: (1) to run a 750-watt cooker for 2½ hr.; (2) to leave a 60-watt lamp on for 24 hr.? (A unit is 1 1000 watt-hours, i.e., the amount of electricity consumed by 1 watt for 1000 hr., or by 1000 watts for 1 hr.)

10. A smoker consumes 6s. 5d. worth of tobacco a week. How much will it cost him if he smokes at the same rate during the months of May, June and July?

The Unitary Method as applied to the solution of problems involving the idea of a complex proportion.

Example 16. If 4 men working 9 hr. a day can do a piece of work in 3 days how many men will be required to do the work in 2 days working 10 hr. a day?

Proceed by thinking only of one pair of similar terms at a time, and finding the effect without regard to any of the other terms. Thus:

To do the work in 3 days at 9 hr. per day 4 men are required.

		1 day at 9	,,	3×4	,,
		1 day at 1	,,	$9 \times 3 \times 4$	,,
		2 days at 1	,,	$\dfrac{9 \times 3 \times 4}{2}$	,,
,,	,,	2 days at 10	,,	$\dfrac{9 \times 3 \times \cancel{4}^{\,2}}{\cancel{10} \times \cancel{2}}_{5}$	,,

$$= \frac{27}{5}$$
$$= 5\tfrac{2}{5} \therefore \text{ 6 men are required.}$$

With a little practice you can shorten this working very considerably by thinking out the effect of two or more of the terms all in the same statement. Thus, we at once reduce the 3 days to the unit 1 and the 9 hr. to the unit 1, and think of the effect as multiplying in the one case by

3 and in the other by 9, which gives the expression $9 \times 3 \times 4$ by one statement instead of by two. In the shortened form the above process would stand thus:

In 3 days of 9 hr. 4 men are required.

$\therefore$,, 1 day of 1   ,, $3 \times 9 \times 4$

$\therefore$,, 2 days of 10   ,, $\dfrac{3 \times 9 \times 4}{2 \times 10,}$ etc.

Example 17. One horse-power will lift 33 000 lb. 1 ft. per minute. How many gallons of water will an engine of 150 horse-power raise to the height of 60 fathoms in 1 day?

Take a gallon of water as equal to 10 lb. avoir.

In 1 min. 1 h.p. lifts through 1 ft. 33 000 lb.;

$\therefore$ in 1 440 min. 150 h.p.

will lift through 360 ft. $\dfrac{33000 \times \overset{4}{\cancel{1440}} \times 150}{\cancel{360}}$ lb.

$= 33\,000 \times 600$ lb.

$= \dfrac{33000 \times \overset{60}{\cancel{600}}}{\cancel{10}}$ gall.

$= 1\,980\,000$ gall.

In the above example the unit is given in each term.

Example 18. A garrison of 1 200 men has provisions for 10 weeks, allowing 9 oz. per man per day. If it is re-inforced by 350 men, what must be the daily allowance per man in order that the provisions may last 12 weeks?

1 200 men can hold out for 10 weeks and receive an allowance of 9 oz. per man per day;

$\therefore$ 1 man can hold out for 1 week and receive an allowance of $(1\,200 \times 10 \times 9)$ oz.;

$\therefore$ 1 550 men can hold out for 12 weeks and receive an allowance of $\dfrac{\overset{300}{\cancel{1200}} \times \cancel{10} \times \overset{3}{\cancel{9}}}{\underset{155}{\cancel{1550}} \times \underset{4}{\cancel{12}}}$ oz. per man per day

$= \dfrac{900}{155}$ oz.

$= \dfrac{180}{31}$ oz.

$= 5\tfrac{25}{31}$ oz.

E

Exercise 33

1. If a man earns £7 in 9 days of 6 hr. each, in how many days of 8 hours can he earn £8?

2. If a 2½ lb. loaf costs 1s. 1d. when wheat is 78s. a qr., how much will a 1½ lb. loaf cost when wheat is 66s. a qr.?

3. If 16½ tons of provisions serve 2 500 men for a fortnight, how much will be required for 3 000 men for 4 weeks?

4. The cost of insuring property worth £500 for two years is 29s. How much would it cost to insure property worth £700 for 1¼ years?

5. If it costs £9 12s. to carry 15¾ tons of coal 36 miles, how much will it cost to carry 6 tons of coal 125 miles?

6. A lawn-mower 16 in. wide and moving at 3 miles per hour cuts a certain lawn in 40 minutes. How long will it take a motor-mower 24 in. wide and travelling at 4 miles per hour to cut a lawn 2¼ times as big?

7. A railway embankment 1½ miles long must be constructed in 30 days, and 400 men are set to work on it. If at the end of 16 days it is found that only 1 050 yd. are finished, how many more men must be put on to finish the work in the stipulated time?

8. A 12-h.p. engine pumps 16 tanks of oil through a height of 270 ft. in 1 hr. 48 min.; how long would it take for a 70-h.p. engine to pump 1 200 tanks of oil through a height of 190 ft.?

9. A family of three can be fed for a year for £110. How much will it cost to feed a family of seven for 5 months? It may be assumed that owing to economies of buying on a larger scale 18s. 10d. in the second case goes as far as £1 in the first.

CHAPTER SEVENTEEN

PROPORTIONAL PARTS

ONE important practical application of the idea and method of proportion is the division of quantities into parts proportional to certain numbers.

Example 1. Water consists of 8 parts by weight of oxygen and 1 of hydrogen. What weight of oxygen is there in 35 grammes of water?

First Method. In any unit of water (it may be a pint, a pound, 35 gallons, etc.) there are 8 parts by weight of oxygen to 1 part of hydrogen. Hence we have to divide the given unit, 35 grammes, in such a way that 8 parts + 1 part shall make up the 35 grammes. Now the total number of parts, viz., 9, must evidently bear the same ratio to 1 (or 8) of these parts as the total number of grammes bears to the number of grammes which the 1 part (or 8) contains, that is—

$$(1) \quad 9 : 1 = 35 : \text{number of grammes in the 1 part};$$
$$\text{or (2)} \quad 9 : 8 = 35 : \text{,,} \qquad \text{,,} \qquad \text{,,} \qquad \text{8 parts};$$

$$\therefore \text{ the 1 part of hydrogen} = \frac{35 \times 1}{9}$$
$$= 3\tfrac{8}{9} \text{ grammes};$$
$$\therefore \text{ the 8 parts of oxygen} = \frac{8 \times 35}{9}$$
$$= \tfrac{280}{9}$$
$$= 31\tfrac{1}{9} \text{ grammes}.$$

Second Method. We have seen that a fraction is one way of expressing a ratio, and every problem dealing with proportional parts can be solved *more rapidly* without the statement of the proportion. Thus, in the above example, the reasoning will be as follows: There are 9 parts in all, 8 out of these 9, or $\frac{8}{9}$, are oxygen, therefore the oxygen in 35 grammes is $\frac{8}{9}$ of $35 = \frac{280}{9} = 31\frac{1}{9}$ grammes.

This is undoubtedly the shorter and more practical way.

The truth of the result can be proved by showing that $31\frac{1}{9}$ is to $3\frac{8}{9}$ as 8 is to 1, and that $31\frac{1}{9} + 3\frac{8}{9} = 35$. Thus:

$$\frac{\frac{280}{9}}{\frac{35}{9}} = \frac{280}{9} \times \frac{9}{35} = \frac{8}{1}, \text{ or } 8 : 1.$$

Note. In taking the first method, a common mistake is to make the statement—

$$8 : 1 = 35 : x,$$

which is untrue; 35 is the value of 9 parts, not of 8 parts; what corresponds to 8 in the statement is $31\frac{1}{9}$; but then this is only found out through the statement—

$$9 : 1 = 35 : x.$$

Example 2. The ratio of the circumference of a circle to its diameter is $355 : 113$. Find the diameter of a circle whose circumference is 20 ft. 8 in.

Here there is no need to add the parts as in the last example. We have simply:

$$\frac{\text{circumference}}{\text{diameter}} = \frac{355}{113},$$

$$\therefore \text{ diameter } = \frac{113}{355} \times 20\frac{2}{3},$$

$$= \frac{113}{355} \times \frac{62}{3},$$

$$= \frac{7\,006}{1\,065},$$

$$= 6 \cdot 578 \text{ ft.}$$

The following is typical of a great many problems connected with commerce:

Example 3. A, B and C join partnership. A contributes £3 000 capital, B £4 050 and C £7 000. The profits of a year's trading amount to £1 075. What is each partner's share?

The assumption, of course, here made is that, all other things being equal, and in the absence of any special agreement, profits should be divided in proportion to the capital of each partner. In the example this proportion is

$$3\ 000 : 4\ 050 : 7\ 000,$$

or, $300 :\ \ 405 :\ \ 700,$

or, $60 :\ \ \ 81 :\ \ 140.$

Hence A's share is 60 parts out of $(60 + 81 + 140)$; and so

$$\text{A's profits} = \tfrac{60}{281} \text{ of } £1\ 075.$$
$$\text{B's} \quad ,, \quad = \tfrac{81}{281} \text{ of } £1\ 075.$$
$$\text{C's} \quad ,, \quad = \tfrac{140}{281} \text{ of } £1\ 075.$$

The following introduces the element of different lengths of time during which the capital is operative:

Example 4. A commences business at the beginning of the year with a capital of £2 400. Three months afterwards he is joined by B with a capital of £2 000. The year's profits are £275; how should they be divided between the two partners?

£2 400 operating for 12 months is the same as
12 × 2 400 or £28 800 operating for 1 *month*,

and £2 000 operating for 9 months is the same as

9 × 2 000 or £18 000 operating for 1 *month*.

Hence the process:

$$\frac{2\,400 \times 12}{2\,000 \times 9} = \frac{28\,800}{18\,000} = \frac{8}{5};$$
$$\therefore \text{ A's profits} = \tfrac{8}{13} \text{ of } \pounds 275$$
$$= \pounds\tfrac{2200}{13}$$
$$= \pounds 169\tfrac{3}{13}$$
$$\therefore \text{ B's profits} = \pounds 105\tfrac{10}{13}.$$

Example 5. Divide £385 of prize money among the captain of a ship, his 2 officers and crew of 8, so that the captain shall have twice as much as each officer and each officer half as much again as each of the crew.

In such a problem it is simplest to begin with the smallest share and represent it by 1. Thus:

Let 1 = seaman's share,
$\therefore 1\tfrac{1}{2}$ = officer's ,,
$\therefore 3$ = captain's ,,

Total of seaman's shares $= 1 \times 8 = 8.$

,, officers' ,, $= 1\tfrac{1}{2} \times 2 = 3.$
,, captain's share $= 3.$

$\therefore$ crew's share $= \dfrac{\overset{4}{\cancel{8}}}{\underset{2}{\cancel{14}}} \text{ of } \pounds\overset{55}{\cancel{385}}$
$= \pounds 220.$

Officers' share $= \dfrac{3}{\underset{2}{\cancel{14}}} \text{ of } \overset{55}{\cancel{385}}$
$= \pounds\tfrac{165}{2}$
$= \pounds 82 \text{ 10s.}$

Captain's share $= \pounds 82 \text{ 10s.}$

Example 6. Divide £350 among 4 people in the proportion of $\tfrac{1}{2}$, $\tfrac{1}{3}$, $\tfrac{1}{4}$ and $\tfrac{1}{5}$. Turn these fractions into other forms having the same denominator; and, since the denominators are equal, the numerators will have the same ratios to one another as the original forms $\frac{1}{2}$, $\frac{1}{3}$, $\frac{1}{4}$ and $\frac{1}{5}$.

Thus: Find L.C.M. = 60,

then $\frac{1}{2} = \frac{30}{60}$, $\frac{1}{3} = \frac{20}{60}$, $\frac{1}{4} = \frac{15}{60}$, $\frac{1}{5} = \frac{12}{60}$.

Hence $\frac{1}{2} : \frac{1}{3} : \frac{1}{4} : \frac{1}{5} :: 30 : 20 : 15 : 12$.

Total number of parts = 77.

$$\therefore \text{ 1st person's share} = \frac{30}{77} \text{ of } \overset{50}{\cancel{£350}}$$
$$= £\frac{1500}{11}$$
$$= £136\frac{4}{11}.$$

2nd   ,,   ,, $= \frac{20}{77}$ of £350.

3rd   ,,   ,, $= \frac{15}{77}$ of £350.

4th   ,,   ,, $= \frac{12}{77}$ of £350.

Exercise 34

1. Divide £60 among three people in the proportion of 3, 4 and 5.

2. Divide £326 among A, B and C, so that A may have twice as much as B and B twice as much as C.

3. Divide a 50 ft. length in the ratio of 12 to 13.

4. A bankrupt's assets amount to £1 375. His seven creditors' claims are respectively £315, £276, £90, £75, £420, £670, £915. What part of the assets should the third creditor get?

5. £1 300 is to be raised as a rate from three villages in proportion to the population. The populations in round numbers are 800, 950, 1 200. What should each village contribute?

6. A starts business with a capital of £750. Six months after he is joined by B with a capital of £350; and nine months after A has started business he is joined by C with a capital of £600. The year's profits are £475. How should they be divided among the three partners?

7. A ship's cargo, worth £4 050, was insured for £3 500. If half of the cargo belonged to A, $\frac{1}{3}$ to B and the rest to C, what would each lose in the event of the vessel being lost?

8. Two graziers rent a field between them for £30 15s. per year. One keeps 12 oxen in it for 7 months, and the other 15 oxen 12 months. What should each pay? (The cost of the grazing of

12 oxen for 7 months is the same as the cost of the grazing of 84 oxen for 1 month.)

9. The main ingredients of a sort of mincemeat are 6 lb. mixed fruit, 1 lb. apples, 2 lb. sugar, ½ lb. almonds, 1 lb. butter. How many pounds of each will be required for 66 lb. mincemeat?

10. Divide £350 15s. among 3 men, 2 women and 5 children, so that each man shall have twice as much as a woman, and each woman as much as 3 children. (If a child's share be denoted by 1, then a woman's share will be denoted by 3 and a man's share by 6.)

11. Divide £78 10s. among 3 people in proportion to the fractions ⅓, ¼ and ⅕.

12. Sugar is composed of 49·856 parts of oxygen, 43·265 parts of carbon and 6·879 parts of hydrogen. How many lb. of carbon are there in 1 cwt. of sugar?

13. The net receipts of a certain Rural District Council are £740. The services administered, and the proportions allotted to them, are as follows:

Housing	3·975 pence
Public Health and Hospitals . .	2·287 ,,
Ditches and Drains . . .	4·102 ,,
Administration	6·031 ,,

Calculate the actual sums allotted to the separate services.

CHAPTER EIGHTEEN

AVERAGES

THE idea of an average enters very largely into commercial and other calculations. The average weight of a racing boat's crew is the weight which each man would be if the total weight of the whole crew were divided *equally* among the several units of the crew. The average run of a train during a journey is that same number of miles the train would have run each hour if the total number of miles were divided *equally* over the number of hours taken.

One object in finding an average is to form a general estimate of a quantity which takes a number of different values. Thus, if a train runs 20 miles in one hour, 40 in another hour, 36 in another hour, 60 in another hour, our idea of its speed is rendered more definite when we say it runs on an average $156 \div 4$, or 39 miles an hour. Another use that an average serves is to *make comparisons easier*. Thus, if a schoolmaster wishes to compare the ages of his pupils in 1940 with the ages of his pupils in 1950 in order to find whether a younger or older class of pupils is attending school, the comparison would be almost impossible without taking the average. Again it may be very useful in various ways to compare the consumption of a certain article per head in one country with its consumption per head in another country. This is done by finding the average. Average, in short, serves much the same purpose as percentage: both fix a *common standard* whereby we make comparisons.

The rule for finding the average is to *add the quantities and divide the sum by their number*. Wherever a "nought" occurs among the quantities, it must be reckoned as forming part of the divisor. Thus, if in a cricket match two batsmen make o each, the sum total of the runs is still divided by 11, not by 9.

EXERCISE 35

1. What is the average of the following lengths: 20 miles, 25 miles, 30 miles, 28 miles, 18 miles?

2. Find the average of 0·6, 1, 0·4, 8·6, 9·1, 12·3.

3. Find the average population of the following towns, whose populations (in thousands) in 1951 were: Glasgow, 1 090; Birmingham 1 112; Liverpool, 790; Manchester, 703; Sheffield, 513; Leeds, 505; and Edinburgh, 467.

4. A cricketer played 12 matches in the season. His runs in the 12 matches were 23, 52, 38, 0, 17, 36, 25, 40, 23, 19, 51, 79. What was his average for the season?

5. A cyclist did 50 miles on Monday, 71 on Tuesday, 40 on Wednesday, rested on Thursday, 59 on Friday and 68 on Saturday. What was his average run per day?

6. What is the average of £3 16s. 2d., £4 12s. 6d., £8 9s., £6 15s. 7d., £2 14s. 6d. and £13 17s. 3d.?

7. A railway incline rises 1 ft. in 70 in the first mile, then 1 in 100 for the next half mile, then 1 in 120 for the next 1 300 yd. Find the average rise in the whole distance.

8. A housekeeper's average weekly outlay on coal is 3s. 6d., on domestic service 9s. 3d., and on personal requirements 4s. 2d. Her weekly allowance is £3, and after 7 weeks she has saved 11s. 4d. What is her average weekly expenditure on the items not specified?

9. A sailing vessel sailed 2 010 miles in 8 days. What was the average rate in miles per hour?

10. The area of Denmark is 17 000 sq. miles, and the average number of people per sq. mile is 202. Corresponding figures for Norway are 125 000 sq. miles and 21, and for Sweden, 173 000 sq. miles and 35. Find the average number of people per sq. mile in the three countries taken together.

11. The temperatures of a certain week as recorded by the thermometer were 61°, 65°, 59°, 66°, 67°, 60°, 61°. What was the average temperature for the week?

(Note that this question may be simplified by subtracting 59° from all the temperatures, finding the average of the quantities left, and adding 59° to it.)

12. A train ran a journey of 726½ miles in 16 hr. 35 min. What was the average run per hour?

13. A family spends equal amounts on Christmas cards at 3d. each, 2d. each and 1d. each. What is the average price of the cards bought? (Be careful.)

14. A car travels equal distances at 30 m.p.h. and 50 m.p.h. What is its average speed?

15. The weights of a boat's crew are respectively 8 st. 12 lb., 9 st., 11st. 5 lb., 12 st. 2 lb., 10 st. 1 lb., 9 st., 9 st. 3 lb., 11 st. 13 lb. What is the average weight of the crew?

16. 10 gall. of a liquid at 28s. per gallon are mixed with 5 gall. at 35s. per gallon. What is the price per gallon of the mixture?

CHAPTER NINETEEN

PERCENTAGES

IF a person invests £375 in one business concern, and gets a dividend of £10 12s., and £420 in another undertaking, which yields him a dividend of £12 13s., he has no means of knowing which is the more profitable investment *unless he can measure his two dividends by some common standard*. The standard found most convenient is 100. Thus by finding what his profit is on £100 of his money in each case, a man knows which is the more profitable. Again, the comparison of increases and decreases in connection with various statistics—population, trade, etc.—is more readily effected and better understood by reference to a common standard, like 100 or 1000. Thus, if the population of a small town rose from 5 915 to 6 512 between the years 1930 and 1940, and from 6 512 to 7 013 between 1940 and 1950, we can best compare the increases of the two periods by finding what was the increase on 100 in each case.

If the increase in the population was at the rate of 10 in every 100, we say that this is 10 per cent. Per cent. (Latin, *per centum*) means "for every hundred". 10 per cent., meaning 10 out of every 100, is the same thing as $\frac{10}{100}$ or $\frac{1}{10}$. It is usually written 10%.

In the case of a population increasing by 10%, we could express this increase by saying the population had increased by $\frac{1}{10}$. The following shows this a little more fully:

100 becomes 110, i.e., increase of 10 on 100 = $\frac{1}{10}$.

200	,,	220	,,	,,	20 ,, 200 = $\frac{1}{10}$.
300	,,	330	,,	,,	30 ,, 300 = $\frac{1}{10}$.
400	,,	440	,,	,,	40 ,, 400 = $\frac{1}{10}$.

etc., etc.

While problems involving "percentage" could always be worked by Rule of Three method, the shortest and most practical method is the fractional, by which every percentage is thought of as a *certain fraction*. Thus think of

1% of a quantity as $\frac{1}{100}$ of it.

2% ,,   ,, $\frac{1}{50}$,,

3% ,,   ,, $\frac{3}{100}$,,

4% ,,   ,, $\frac{1}{25}$,,

5% ,,   ,, $\frac{1}{20}$,,

6% ,,   ,, $\frac{3}{50}$,,

EXERCISE 36

Express as fractions:

1. 60%.
2. 75%.
3. 5%.
4. 40%.
5. $8\frac{1}{3}\%$.
6. 8%.
7. $2\frac{1}{2}\%$.
8. $2\frac{3}{4}\%$.

9. $1\frac{1}{4}\%$.
10. 100%.
11. $18\frac{3}{4}\%$.
12. $\frac{2}{3}\%$.
13. $\frac{1}{8}\%$.
14. $7\frac{1}{2}\%$.
15. 150%.

Express as percentages:

16. $\frac{1}{2}$, $\frac{1}{3}$, $\frac{1}{4}$, $\frac{1}{5}$, $\frac{1}{6}$.

17. $\frac{2}{3}$, $\frac{3}{4}$, $\frac{9}{10}$, $\frac{5}{8}$, $\frac{3}{5}$.

18. $\frac{2}{5}$, $\frac{8}{9}$, $\frac{4}{5}$, $\frac{7}{8}$, 0.5.

19. 0.75, 3, $\frac{1}{40}$, $\frac{1}{50}$, 0.375.

20. $\frac{3}{50}$, $\frac{5}{4}$, $\frac{6}{5}$, 0.25, 0.45.

The following methods in dealing with some percentages should be noticed:

$$5\% = \tfrac{1}{20} = 1\text{s. in the } \pounds.$$
$$2\tfrac{1}{2}\% = \tfrac{1}{40} = 6\text{d.} \quad \text{,,}$$
$$\tfrac{1}{8}\% = \tfrac{1}{800} = \tfrac{3}{10}\text{d.} \quad \text{,,}$$

Example 1. Find the value of 5% of £1 764 18s. 9d.

$$
\begin{array}{llll}
5\% \text{ of } £1\ 764 = & 1\ 764\text{s.} = £88 & 4 & 0 \\
\text{,,} \qquad \text{ros.} = & 6\text{d.} = 0 & 0 & 6 \\
\text{,,} \quad 8\text{s. } 9\text{d.} = \tfrac{1}{20} \text{ of } 8\text{s. } 9\text{d.} = & 0 & 0 & 5\tfrac{1}{4} \\
\hline
& £88 & 4 & 11\tfrac{1}{4}
\end{array}
$$

Example 2. Find the value of $2\tfrac{1}{2}\%$ of £875 12s. 6d.

$$
\begin{array}{llll}
2\tfrac{1}{2}\% \text{ of } £875 = 437\text{s. } 6\text{d.} = £21 & 17 & 6 \\
\text{,,} \qquad \text{ros.} = & 3\text{d.} = 0 & 0 & 3 \\
\text{,,} \quad 2\text{s. } 6\text{d.} = \tfrac{1}{4} \text{ of } 3\text{d.} = & 0 & 0 & 0\tfrac{3}{4} \\
\hline
& £21 & 17 & 9\tfrac{3}{4}
\end{array}
$$

EXERCISE 37

1. Find the value of 5% of £72; £84 10s.; £70 17s. 6d.; £63; £1 975 8s.; 1 800 yd.; 10 tons 2 cwt.; 1 mile; 30 hr.; 1 600 yd.
2. Find the value of $2\tfrac{1}{2}\%$ of £600; £300; £975; £61 17s.; £80¼; 350 yd.; 45 oz. Troy; 1 200 sheep; 875 acres; 10 quarters of wheat.
3. Find the value of 10% of £16 16s.; £18 19s. 7d.; £17 13s. 4d.; £2 15s.; £327 15s. 9d.
4. Find the value of $3\tfrac{1}{2}\%$ of £18; £3 005; £6 5s.; 10s.; £81 9s.
5. Find the value of $33\tfrac{1}{3}\%$ of £45; £94 10s.; £275 13s. 5d.; £172 12s. 7d.; £16 13s.

Example 3. What percentage of 60 is 2?

$$
\begin{array}{c}
2 \text{ is } \tfrac{2}{60} \text{ or } \tfrac{1}{30} \text{ of } 60, \text{ and} \\
\tfrac{1}{30} \text{ of } 100 = 3\tfrac{1}{3}: \\
\therefore \ 2 \text{ is } 3\tfrac{1}{3}\% \text{ of } 60.
\end{array}
$$

EXERCISE 38

What per cent. is:

1. £3 of £12.
2. £5 of £45.
3. 1s. of £1.
4. 6d. of £2.
5. £25 of £125.
6. 3 of 6.
7. 2 of 50.
8. ¾ of 1.

9. 3s. of £1.
10. 2s. of 30s.
11. 3 yd. of 60 yd.
12. 1 cwt. of 2 tons.
13. £5 of £40.
14. 1 of 2½.
15. 7 of 63.
16. 1 of 0·5.

Worked Examples

Worked examples of some of the most typical applications of "percentages".

1. The population of a town increases in 2 years from 130 050 to 132 651; what is the rate per cent. of this increase?

$$\text{Actual increase} = 132\ 651 - 130\ 050$$
$$= 2\ 601 \text{ on } 130\ 050;$$
$$\therefore \text{ increase per cent.} = \frac{2\ 601}{130\ 050} \text{ of } 100$$
$$= \frac{2\ 601}{1\ 300\cdot5}$$
$$= 2.$$

2. 1 lb. of standard silver is coined into 66s. Find the profit per cent. when standard silver is worth 5s. 0½d. per oz.

$$1 \text{ lb. of silver} = 12 \text{ oz.};$$
$$\therefore \text{ value of 1 lb. of silver} = 12 \times 5\text{s. } 0\frac{1}{2}\text{d.}$$
$$= 60\text{s. } 6\text{d.};$$
$$\therefore \text{ gain} = 5\text{s. } 6\text{d. on } 60\text{s. } 6\text{d.};$$

$$\therefore \text{ gain per cent.} = \frac{5\frac{1}{2}}{60\frac{1}{2}} \times 100$$
$$= \frac{11}{2} \times \frac{2}{121} \times 100$$
$$= \frac{100}{11}$$
$$= 9\frac{1}{11}.$$

3. The gross receipts of a company are £485 000; of these 40% is taken for working expenses, and 55% as a dividend of $3\frac{1}{2}\%$ on the capital of the company. How much is paid for working expenses, how much to the shareholders, and what is the capital?

$$\text{Working expenses} = 40\% \text{ of } £485\ 000$$
$$= \frac{4}{10} \times 485\ 000$$
$$= £194\ 000.$$
$$\text{Total dividend} = \frac{55}{100} \text{ of } 485\ 000$$
$$= 55 \times 4\ 850$$
$$= £266\ 750.$$

Of this dividend every £$3\frac{1}{2}$ represents £100 capital;

$$\therefore \text{ capital} = \frac{266\ 750}{3\frac{1}{2}} \times £100$$
$$= \frac{£26\ 675\ 000 \times 2}{7}$$
$$= \frac{£53\ 350\ 000}{7}$$
$$= £7\ 621\ 428 \text{ (approx.)}.$$

4. At what rate per cent. is the deduction made when 19s. $10\frac{1}{2}$d. is taken from an account of £39 15s. in consideration of immediate payment?

$$\text{Rate per cent.} = \frac{19s.\ 10\frac{1}{2}d.}{£39\ 15s.} \text{ of } 100$$
$$= \frac{19\frac{7}{8}s.}{795s.} \times 100$$
$$= \frac{159 \times \overset{20}{\cancel{100}}}{8 \times \cancel{795}}$$
$$= 2\frac{1}{2}.$$

5. A manufacturer combines 3 gall. of a mixture, which contains 15% of water, with 2 gall. of one containing 10% of water, and adds 1 gall. of water. Find the percentage of water in the resulting mixture.

Water in first mixture	$= \frac{15}{100}$ of 3 gall.
	$= \frac{9}{20}$ gall.
Water in second mixture	$= \frac{1}{10}$ of 2 gall.
	$= \frac{1}{5}$ gall.
Water added	$= 1$ gall.
$\therefore$ Total amount of water in the final mixture of 6 gall.	$= (\frac{9}{20} + \frac{1}{5} + 1)$ gall.
	$= 1\frac{13}{20}$ gall.
$\therefore$ Percentage of water in final mixture	$= \dfrac{1\frac{13}{20}}{6}$ of 100

$$= \frac{\overset{11}{\cancel{33}} \times \overset{5}{\cancel{100}}}{\underset{2}{\cancel{20} \times \cancel{6}}}$$

$$= \frac{55}{2}$$

$$= 27\frac{1}{2}.$$

EXERCISE 39

1. The population of a town in 1921 was 156 014; in 1931 it had risen to 190 050. Find the approximate increase per cent.
2. In a school of 960 pupils, 500 are girls, the rest are boys. What is the percentage of boys and girls respectively?
3. Of an army of 37 000 men 1 855 are in hospital. What percentage is fit for duty?
4. In a certain town of 85 016 inhabitants the deaths for a certain week were 325. What is the rate per thousand per annum?
5. A rate collector charges $2\frac{1}{2}$% for collecting rates. How much should he receive for collecting £1 356?
6. The rateable value of a house is four-fifths of the rent, which is £52 a year. The water rate is $12\frac{1}{2}$% of the rateable value. What is the payment each quarter for water rate?
7. A fire-insurance premium is $\frac{3}{16}$% of the value of the property insured. What is the premium on £1 240?
8. Gunpowder is made of 75% nitre, 15% carbon and 10% sulphur. Find the weight of each ingredient in 1 cwt. of gunpowder.

9. Three partners have capitals of £7 400, £6 000 and £4 600 invested in a business. The first charge on the profits is 5% for depreciation of capital; after this £200 is paid to each of the partners for management; and the remainder is divided proportionally between the partners. If the profits for a certain year are £2 310, what does each partner receive? (5% interest on capital means that for every £100 of capital £5 is deducted from the profits.)

10. A mass of auriferous sand, weighing 12 cwt. (avoirdupois), is known to contain 3·8% of gold. From this $\frac{11}{12}$ of the sand is removed by washing, and the part removed is found to contain only 0·6% of gold. How many lb. troy of gold are contained in the remaining cwt.?

11. There are 156 boys in the junior and 162 in the senior department of a school. If the boys constitute 65% of the scholars in the junior department and 45% of those in the senior department, what percentage are they of the whole school?

12. A man has a garden of $1\frac{1}{8}$ acres. He has an orchard of 1 350 sq. yd. and a tennis-court of 600 sq. yd. 1% of the total area is occupied by a rockery. What percentage remains?

13. A certain factory burns $5\frac{1}{2}$ tons of coal per day. By an alteration in the furnace this amount is reduced to $4\frac{1}{2}$ tons per day. What percentage of saving is effected?

14. A commercial traveller receives as commission $2\frac{1}{2}$% on all his business beyond £500. In a certain year he receives orders for £3 050 17s. 6d. What commission does he receive?

15. Out of a family's total expenditure of £360 17s. 6d. in a certain period, the food item was £72 16s. 4d., house expenses £48 14s. 9d., rent and taxes £88 15s. 6d., amusements £19 0s. 10d. Express these as percentages of the total.

16. A cargo is valued at £3 070 10s., the premium on insurance is 5%, policy duty 4s.%, and commission $\frac{1}{2}$%. What sum must be insured to cover the cargo and the expenses of insurance, and what is the premium?

17. What is the sum to be paid for insuring a cargo worth £2 715, the premium being 30s., policy duty 3s., and agent's commission $\frac{1}{8}$%?

18. In a certain year the total number of occupied males over 12 years old in Greater London was 2 298 903, and the total number unoccupied was 369 396. Express the number of unoccupied males as a percentage of the total number.

19. In 1923 Great Britain produced 282·6 and the U.S.A. 581·5 million metric tonnes of coal. The U.S.A.'s percentage of the world's total production was 49·12; what was Great Britain's percentage?

CHAPTER TWENTY

AREAS OF RECTANGULAR FIGURES

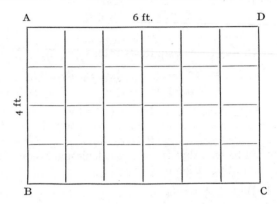

In the above diagram AD represents 6 ft. and AB 4 ft. It will be seen that the rectangle ABCD contains 24 smaller areas each 1 ft. in length each way. In other words the rectangle 6 ft. long by 4 ft. broad contains 24 sq. ft.

Now, suppose we take a rectangle 4½ ft. by 3¼ ft.

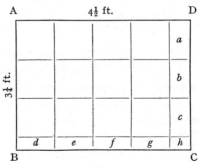

(1) The areas a, b, c are each half of the larger areas, therefore each $= \frac{1}{2}$ sq. ft.

(2) The areas d, e, f, g are each one-fourth of the larger areas, therefore each $= \frac{1}{4}$ sq. ft.

(3) The area $h =$ half of the area g
$\qquad\qquad = \frac{1}{2}$ of $\frac{1}{4}$, or $\frac{1}{8}$ sq. ft.

Therefore, in the rectangle there are
12 sq. ft. $+ 3$ times $\frac{1}{2}$ sq. ft. $+ 4$ times $\frac{1}{4}$ sq. ft. $+ \frac{1}{8}$ sq. ft.

$\qquad = (12 + 1\frac{1}{2} + 1 + \frac{1}{8})$ sq. ft.
$\qquad = 14\frac{5}{8}$ sq. ft.

Now, $4\frac{1}{2} \times 3\frac{1}{4} = \frac{9}{2} \times \frac{13}{4} = \frac{117}{8} = 14\frac{5}{8}$.

Hence the *area* of any *rectangular* shape is found by *multiplying the length by the breadth.*

It can be seen that the above calculation is equivalent to the multiplication of $4\frac{1}{2}$ by $3\frac{1}{4}$:

$(4 + \frac{1}{2})(3 + \frac{1}{4}) = (4 \times 3) + (\frac{1}{2} \times 3) + (4 \times \frac{1}{4}) + (\frac{1}{2} \times \frac{1}{4}).$

In working problems connected with areas the following points must be clearly understood:

1. Linear measure $\times$ linear measure $=$ square measure
$\qquad\qquad$ The diagram shows this.

2. Linear measure $\div$ linear measure $=$ a number of times, or simply a number.
$\qquad\qquad$ Thus, 10 ft. $\div$ 5 ft. $= 2$.

3. Square measure $\div$ linear measure $=$ linear measure.
$\qquad\qquad$ This follows from 1.

4. Square measure $\div$ square measure $=$ a number.
$\qquad\qquad$ Thus, 30 sq. ft. $\div$ 5 sq. ft. $= 6$.

Or—
$\qquad$ 1. Ft. $\times$ ft. $=$ sq. ft.
$\qquad\qquad$ Yd. $\times$ yd. $=$ sq. yd., etc.

2. Ft. ÷ ft. = a number.
3. Sq. ft. ÷ linear ft. = linear ft.
   Sq. yd. ÷ linear yd. = linear yd., etc.
4. Sq. ft. ÷ sq. ft. = a number.
   Sq. yd. ÷ sq. yd. = a number, etc.

How to find the area of the walls of a room:

Let l represent length of room,
  b ,, breadth ,,
  h ,, height ,,

Then, area of long wall = $l \times h$;
∴ ,, 2 long walls = $2lh$,
  ,, short wall = $b \times h$;
∴ ,, 2 short walls = $2bh$;
∴ ,, 4 walls = $2lh + 2bh$
        = $2h(l + b)$.

Or, if the 4 walls be thought of as in one straight line
then the area of the four = $(l + b + l + b) \times h$
         = $(2l + 2b)h$
         = $2(l + b)h$,
which is the same as $2h(l + b)$.

The following diagram illustrates the above:

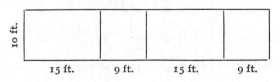

Area = {(15 + 9 + 15 + 9) × 10} sq. ft.
  = {2(15 + 9) × 10} sq. ft.
  = 480 sq. ft.

The area of the sides of a cistern is calculated in the same way: the four sides corresponding to the walls of a room, and the top and bottom to the ceiling and floor.

In working problems keep in mind the following also:

$$\text{(1) length} \times \text{breadth} = \text{area};$$
$$\text{hence (2) length} = \text{area} \div \text{breadth};$$
$$\text{,, (3) breadth} = \text{area} \div \text{length}.$$

Example 1. Find the area of a rectangular plot of ground whose length is 20 yd. and breadth $12\frac{1}{2}$ yd.

$$\text{Area} = 20 \text{ yd.} \times 12\frac{1}{2} \text{ yd.}$$
$$= (20 \times 12\frac{1}{2}) \text{ sq. yd.}$$
$$= 250 \text{ sq. yd.}$$

Example 2. Find the cost of papering the walls of a room whose length is $20\frac{1}{2}$ ft., breadth 16 ft. and height $9\frac{1}{2}$ ft., with paper whose width is $22\frac{1}{2}$ in., at 1s. 6d. per yd.

$$\text{Area of walls} = 2h(l + b)$$
$$= \{(2 \times 9\frac{1}{2}) \times (20\frac{1}{2} + 16)\} \text{ sq. ft.}$$
$$= \{19 \times 36\frac{1}{2}\} \text{ sq. ft.}$$
$$= (19 \times \tfrac{73}{2}) \text{ sq. ft.}$$

Length of paper wanted—

$$= \text{total area of walls} \div \text{breadth of paper}$$
$$= \left(19 \times \frac{73}{2}\right) \text{ sq. ft.} \div \frac{22\frac{1}{2}}{12} \text{ ft.}$$
$$= \left(19 \times \frac{73}{2} \times \frac{24}{45}\right) \text{ ft.}$$
$$= \left(19 \times \frac{73}{2} \times \frac{24}{45} \times \frac{1}{3}\right) \text{ yd.};$$
$$\therefore \text{ cost} = \left(19 \times \frac{73}{2} \times \frac{8}{15} \times \frac{1}{3} \times \frac{3}{40}\right) £$$
$$= £\frac{1\,387}{150}$$
$$= £9 \text{ 4s. } 11\frac{1}{3}\text{d.}$$

Example 3. The interior measurements of a rectangular box are 12 ft. 6 in., 10 ft. 8 in. and 7 ft. 6 in. Find the cost of lining the box (including the lid) with metal at 1s. 6d. per square foot.

Area to be lined—

= area of 4 sides + area of top + area of bottom
= $2h(l + b)$ + $(l \times b)$ + $(l \times b)$
= $(2 \times 7\frac{1}{2}) \times 23\frac{1}{6} + (12\frac{1}{2} \times 10\frac{2}{3}) + (12\frac{1}{2} \times 10\frac{2}{3})$,

$$= \left(\overset{5}{\cancel{15}} \times \frac{139}{6}\right) + \left(2 \times \frac{25}{2} \times \frac{32}{3}\right)$$

$$= (\frac{695}{2} \times \frac{\overset{2}{800}}{3}) \text{ sq. ft.}$$

$$= \frac{2\,085 + 1\,600}{6} \text{ sq. ft.}$$

$$= \tfrac{3685}{6} \text{ sq. ft.}$$

$\therefore$ cost $= £(\tfrac{3685}{6} \times \tfrac{3}{40})$
$= £46$ 1s. 3d.

Example 4. Find the cost of the paper required for a room 19 ft. 9 in. long, 16 ft. 3 in. broad and 11 ft. high, if the paper be 2 ft. 9 in. broad, and cost 3s. 6d. per piece of 12 yd., assuming that $\frac{1}{6}$ of the surface of the walls is not to be covered.

Area of walls	$= 2h(l + b)$
	$= (22 \times 36)$ sq. ft.
	$= 792$ sq. ft.
Actual area to be papered	$= (792 - \frac{1}{6}$ of $792)$ sq. ft.
	$= (792 - 132)$ sq. ft.
	$= 660$ sq. ft.
Length of paper required	$= (660 \div 2\frac{3}{4})$ ft.
	$= (660 \times \frac{4}{11})$ ft.
	$= 240$ ft.
	$= 80$ yd.;

∴ number of pieces 12 yd. long required—

$$= \tfrac{80}{12}$$
$$= 6\tfrac{2}{3}$$

∴ *whole* number of pieces required—

$$= 7$$

∴ cost $= 7 \times$ 3s. 6d.
                 $= £1$ 4s. 6d.

Example 5. A room is 20 ft. long, $15\tfrac{1}{2}$ ft. wide. It is to be covered with carpet so as to leave a stained border all round the room 2ft. wide. How many yards of carpet $\tfrac{3}{4}$ yd. wide will be required to cover the part to be carpeted, and how many square yards of staining will there be?

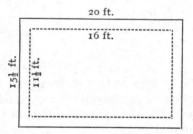

The diagram shows how to proceed in this kind of problem. As the area of the stained portion is evidently the difference between the *total* area of $20 \times 15\tfrac{1}{2}$ and the *inside* area of $16 \times 11\tfrac{1}{2}$, the easiest method of finding the area of the stained portion is to find the areas of total and inside measurements, and subtract the one from the other.

Total area $= 20 \times 15\tfrac{1}{2} = 310$ sq. ft.
Inside area $= 16 \times 11\tfrac{1}{2} = 184$ sq. ft.
∴ area of stained portion $= 126$ sq. ft.

(1)   Carpeted area $= \frac{184}{9}$ sq. yd.

∴ length of carpet required $= \left(\frac{184}{9} \div \frac{3}{4}\right)$ yd.

$$= \left(\frac{184}{9} \times \frac{4}{3}\right) \text{ yd.}$$

$$= \frac{736}{27} \text{ yd.}$$

$$= 27\frac{7}{27} \text{ yd.}$$

(2)   Stained area $= \frac{126}{9}$ sq. yd.

$$= 14 \text{ sq. yd.}$$

Example 6. How many square yards of glass will be required for 200 roof-lights of a station, the light space-measurement being 12 ft. long and 20 in. wide; but instead of the glass being glazed in one piece of 12 ft. long, it is to be in three pieces with overlaps of not less than 3 in., and an overlap of $4\frac{1}{2}$ in. over the bottom of the woodwork of the sash?

To satisfy the conditions of overlapping, etc., the length of each roof-light

$$= 12 \text{ ft.} + 6 \text{ in. (2 overlaps)} + 4\frac{1}{2} \text{ in.}$$

$$= 12 \text{ ft. } 10\frac{1}{2} \text{ in.}$$

∴ Area of 1 roof-light $= \left(12\frac{21}{24} \times \frac{20}{12}\right)$ sq. ft.

$$= \left(12\frac{7}{8} \times \frac{5}{3}\right) \text{ sq. ft.}$$

$$= \left(\frac{103}{8} \times \frac{5}{3} \times \frac{1}{9}\right) \text{ sq. yd.}$$

∴ Area of 200 roof-lights $= \left(100 \times \frac{103}{8} \times \frac{5}{3} \times \frac{1}{9}\right)$ sq. yd.

$$= \frac{25 \times 103 \times 5}{27} \text{ sq. yd.}$$

$$= \frac{12\,875}{27} \text{ sq. yd.}$$

$$= 477 \text{ sq. yd. (nearly).}$$

EXERCISE 40

1. Find the area of a rectangular garden plot 8 yd. by $5\frac{1}{2}$ yd.
2. Find the area of a floor 18 ft. by $12\frac{1}{3}$ ft.
3. How many square yards of linoleum will be required to cover a lobby $10\frac{1}{2}$ ft. long and $4\frac{1}{3}$ ft. broad?

4. Find the area in acres of a field whose length is 8 chains 70 links and breadth 5 chains 40 links.

5. How many yards of paper $\frac{7}{8}$ yd. wide will be required for the walls of a room 20 ft. long, 18 ft. wide and $12\frac{1}{2}$ ft. high?

6. How many yards of carpet 2 ft. wide will cover a floor 28 ft. long and $25\frac{1}{2}$ ft. broad?

7. Find the cost of covering a floor whose dimensions are $18\frac{3}{4}$ ft. and 12 ft. with linoleum $\frac{3}{4}$ yd. wide at 3s. 6d. per yd.

8. Find the cost of papering the walls of a room whose dimensions are 30 ft., 25 ft. and $15\frac{1}{2}$ ft. with paper $2\frac{1}{4}$ ft. wide at 2s. 6d. a yard.

9. Find the cost of papering the same room (Ex. 8) with paper 21 in. wide at 2s. 3d. a yard, allowing for three windows each 6 ft. by 3 ft., and two doors each 8 ft. by 4 ft.

10. How many square feet of glass are required to glaze six windows, each containing 12 panes of glass, and each pane measuring 18 in. by 6 in.?

11. A Turkey carpet $16\frac{1}{2}$ ft. by 14 ft. is laid on a floor $25\frac{1}{4}$ ft. by $18\frac{1}{4}$ ft.; find the cost of staining the rest of the floor at 5d. per square yard.

12. A rectangular room is 30 ft. long and 25 ft. wide, and the height from the top of the skirting to the cornice is 10 ft. How many yards of paper 21 in. wide will be required to cover the walls, assuming that the paper saved by doors, windows and other openings will just balance the waste caused by the necessity of matching the patterns?

13. Find the cost of covering the inside of an open cistern 4 ft. long, 3 ft. wide and 4 ft. deep, with lead weighing 7 lb. to the sq. ft., at £4 4s. per cwt.

14. A lawn 40 yd. long and 35 yd. broad is to be turfed with sods 3 ft. by 1 ft. at 24s. per 100 sods. Find the cost.

15. A room is 35 ft. long and 28 ft. broad. There is to be a stained border all round the room $2\frac{1}{2}$ ft. wide. How many yards of carpet 2 ft. wide will be required for the part of the floor to be carpeted; and what will be the cost of staining the border at $4\frac{1}{2}$d. per square yard.

16. Find the rent at £7 an acre of a rectangular park 750 yd. long and 350 yd. wide.

17. How many pieces of paper 12 yd. long and 21 in. wide will be required for a room of the following dimensions: $l = 20$ yd., $b = 16$ yd., $h = 5\frac{1}{2}$ yd.; and what will be the cost at 3s. per yd.?

18. In a courtyard $60\frac{1}{2}$ ft. long and 40 ft. wide there is a footway 5 ft. wide running the whole length of the yard. What is the cost of paving the whole, the price per sq. yd. for the footway being 5s. 6d., and for the remainder 4s. 6d.?

19. What will it cost (a) in francs, (b) in English money, to carpet a floor 10 m. by 8 m. with carpet $\frac{2}{3}$ m. wide, at 500 francs per metre? (988 francs per £1.)

20. A house is re-plastered on three sides. It stands on a base 44 ft. square, and is 21 ft. high. Two of the sides have four

windows each, the other only two, and these each measure 6 ft. by 4 ft. What is the total cost, at 9s. 6d. per sq. yd.?

21. A map measures 4 ft. 6 in. by 3 ft. 3 in., and is drawn on a scale of ⅓ in. to the mile; how many acres does the map represent?

22. A rectangular piece of land is 1 300 links in length and 800 in breadth; how many square feet would be occupied on paper by a plan of the land drawn on a scale of 1½ in. to the chain?

23. A room is 24¼ ft. long, 19½ ft. wide and 12 ft. high; what is the difference in cost of papering the walls with English paper 21 in. wide, and costing 2s. 3d. a yd., and with French paper 18 in. wide, and costing 2s. a yd.?

CHAPTER TWENTY-ONE

VOLUMES OF RECTANGULAR SOLIDS

THE following diagram will explain the reason of the rule for finding the volume or content of any rectangular solid:

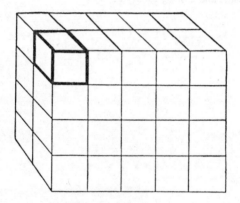

This diagram represents a solid body, 5 ft. by 4 ft. by 2 ft., which has been divided into cubes with 1-ft. sides. The reader will see that there are 2 columns of 5 times 4 cubes, or 40 cubes in all. Hence the rule: To find volume or content of a rectangular solid, multiply length, breadth and thickness together.

As in the measurement of areas, note the following in connection with volumes:

1. Cubic measure ÷ cubic measure = a number of times.

2. Cubic measure ÷ square measure = linear measure.

3. Cubic measure ÷ linear measure = square measure.

Example 1. Find the volume of a block of wood measuring 6 ft. 8 in. long, 2 ft. wide and $1\frac{1}{2}$ in. thick.

$$\text{Volume} = \text{length} \times \text{breadth} \times \text{thickness}$$

$$= \left(6\tfrac{8}{12} \times 2 \times \frac{1\frac{1}{2}}{12}\right) \text{ cu. ft.}$$

$$= \left(\frac{\overset{5}{\cancel{20}}}{3} \times 2 \times \frac{3}{24}\right) \text{ cu. ft.}$$

$$\underset{\underset{3}{\big|}}{12}$$

$$= \tfrac{5}{3}, \text{ or } 1\tfrac{2}{3} \text{ cu. ft.}$$

Example 2. If a gallon of water weighs 10 lb., and 1 cu. ft. of water weighs $62\frac{1}{2}$ lb., how many gallons can be held in a cistern 10 ft. long, $5\frac{1}{2}$ ft. wide and $3\frac{1}{2}$ ft. deep?

$$\text{Volume of cistern} = (10 \times 5\tfrac{1}{2} \times 3\tfrac{1}{2}) \text{ cu. ft.}$$

Now, in 1 cu. ft. of water there are $62\frac{1}{2}$ lb., or $\dfrac{62\frac{1}{2}}{10}$ gall.

$\therefore$ number of gallons cistern

$$\text{will hold} = \cancel{10} \times 5\tfrac{1}{2} \times 3\tfrac{1}{2} \times \frac{62\frac{1}{2}}{\cancel{10}}$$

$$= \tfrac{11}{2} \times \tfrac{7}{2} \times \tfrac{125}{2}$$

$$= \tfrac{9625}{8}$$

$$= 1\,203\tfrac{1}{8} \text{ gall.}$$

Example 3. A cistern 10 ft. long, 7 ft. broad and 5 ft. deep is filled with water which runs into it at the rate of 8 ft. per second through a pipe whose section is $\frac{3}{4}$ of a square inch. How long will it take to fill?

$$\text{Volume of cistern} = (10 \times 7 \times 5) \text{ cu. ft.}$$
$$= 350 \text{ cu. ft.}$$

Volume of water passing through

$$\text{pipe per second} = 8 \text{ ft.} \times \tfrac{3}{4} \text{ sq. in.}$$

$$= 8 \text{ ft.} \times \frac{\tfrac{3}{4}}{144} \text{ sq. ft.}$$

$$= \overset{2}{8} \times \frac{3}{\underset{\underset{24}{72}}{4 \times 144}}$$

$$= \tfrac{1}{24} \text{ cu. ft.};$$

∴ time in which

$$\text{cistern will fill} = (350 \text{ cu. ft.} \div \tfrac{1}{24} \text{ cu. ft.}) \text{ sec.}$$

$$= (350 \times 24) \text{ sec.}$$

$$= \frac{350 \times \overset{}{24}}{\underset{150}{3\,600}} \text{ hr.}$$

$$= 2\tfrac{1}{3} \text{ hr.}$$

Example 4. A section of a stream is 10 ft. wide and 1 ft. deep. The mean flow of the water through the section is $2\frac{1}{2}$ miles an hour. Taking the volume of 25 gall. to equal 4 cu. ft., how many gallons of water flow through the section in a day?

$$\text{Area of section} = (10 \times 1) \text{ sq. ft.}$$

$$= 10 \text{ sq. ft.}$$

$$\text{Length of column of water} = (24 \times 2\tfrac{1}{2}) \text{ miles}$$

$$= 60 \text{ miles};$$

∴ volume of water passing

$$\text{through section in 1 day} = 60 \text{ miles} \times 10 \text{ sq. ft.}$$

$$= (60 \times 5\,280 \times 10) \text{ cu. ft.}$$

$$= 3\,168\,000 \text{ cu. ft.}$$

$$\text{But volume of 4 cu. ft.} = 25 \text{ gall.};$$

$$\therefore \text{ volume of 1 cu. ft.} = \tfrac{25}{4} \text{ gall.};$$

∴ volume of 3 168 000

$$\text{cu. ft.} = \frac{3\ 168\ 000 \times 25}{4} \text{ gall.}$$

$$= 792\ 000 \times 25 \text{ gall.}$$

$$= 19\ 800\ 000 \text{ gall.}$$

EXERCISE 41

1. Find the volume of water in a full cistern whose length is 7 ft., breadth 5½ ft. and depth 6 ft.

2. How many cubic feet of soil can be taken from a rectangular railway cutting 750 ft. long, 12½ ft. broad and 25 ft. deep?

3. If a cubic foot weighs 1 000 oz., what is the weight of water in a cistern which is 10 ft. long, 7 ft. broad and 3½ ft. deep?

4. Find the value of a stack 25 ft. by 18 ft. by 10 ft. 6 in. of bricks each 9 in. by 4 in. by 3 in. at £8 6s. 8d. per 1 000 bricks.

5. What must be the length of a trench 16 ft. wide and 15 ft. deep so that it may hold 50 000 gall of water, the cubical measure of a gallon being equal to 277·274 cu. in.?

6. A river 12 ft. deep, 90 yd. broad flows at the rate of 2½ miles an hour; how many gallons pass a certain point per minute? (Given 1 cu. ft. = 6·23 gall.)

7. How many cubic feet of lead $\frac{1}{12}$ in. thick will be required to cover the sides and bottom of a cistern 10 ft. long, 6 ft. wide and 6 ft. deep?

8. A plate of gold 6 in. square and $\frac{1}{8}$ in. thick is hammered out so as to cover a surface of 3 sq. yd. Find its present thickness.

9. A block of steel 1 ft. 3 in. long, 10 in. broad and 9 in. deep is rolled out into a rod which has a uniform section of 1·08 sq. in. Find the length of the rod in yards, feet and inches.

10. If a piece of ground an acre in extent be flooded by 2 000 tons of water, find the average depth of the water in inches. (1 cu. ft. of water weighs 1 000 oz.)

11. Given that ice is $\frac{9}{10}$ as heavy as water, how many tons of ice can be packed into an ice-store 20 ft. by 18 ft. by 12 ft.?

12. A reservoir is 24 ft. 3 in. long and 12 ft. wide. How many tons of water must be drawn off in order that the surface of the water may fall 5 ft.?

CHAPTER TWENTY-TWO

AREAS AND VOLUMES OF COMMON FIGURES

THE formulae in this chapter cannot be proved without some study of Geometry. Most of them can easily be verified by experiment, and they are given here merely for practical use; anyone who wishes to understand the theory, or to study more complex figures, would be well advised to read *Teach Yourself Geometry*, a companion volume to this one, where these topics are fully discussed.

Triangle

The area of the *triangle* ABC in the figure is equal to half the area of the *parallelogram* ABCD, and the latter area $= b \times h$ (square units).

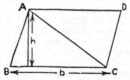

Thus area of triangle $= \frac{1}{2}bh = \frac{1}{2} \times$ base $\times$ height.

Note that any of the sides of a triangle may be considered to be the base. If one of the angles of the triangle is a *right-angle* (see fig.), then the area is simply half the product of the two sides at right angles.

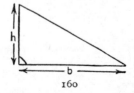

The area of any figure bounded entirely by straight lines can be found by dividing the figure into triangles and finding their areas separately.

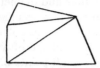

An especially important area is that of the *trapezium*, such a figure as that shown in the diagram PQRS. It will be seen that this can be divided into two triangles,

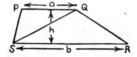

each of height h, PQS and QSR. Their areas are $\frac{1}{2}ah$ and $\frac{1}{2}bh$ respectively, so that the area of the whole figure is $\frac{1}{2}(a + b) \times h$.

Circle

The only other area we shall mention is that of the circle. The area of a circle is πr^2, where r is the radius (see diagram), and π (Greek "pi") is the symbol always used to represent a certain number which cannot be

expressed accurately as a fraction: approximate values for it are $\frac{22}{7}$, 3·14, or 3·142. A more accurate value is 3·14159. This number is also useful in finding the

F

circumference (the boundary ABDC of the circle). The length of the circumference is $2\pi r$, or πd, where d stands for *diameter* (AD in the diagram). Note carefully the difference between radius and diameter.

When we come to consider volumes, one simple principle enables us to apply the formulae for areas in many cases. This is that the volume of any solid which has the same *cross-section* at all points of its length is equal to length × area of cross-section. The cross-section of a solid is the figure obtained by making a flat (or plane) cut in any direction. Thus, a *cylinder* can be cut as shown in the diagram so that its cross-sections are all

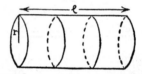

equal circles, and its volume is therefore $\pi r^2 l$, where r is the radius of the circle of cross-section and l is its length. Or again, a greenhouse standing against a wall has very often a constant cross-section of the shape shown in the diagram, that is, a trapezium cross-section.

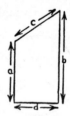

The volume of such a greenhouse is $\frac{1}{2}(a + b) \times d \times l$, where l stands for its length, not shown in the diagram.

The surface areas of such solids can also be found by a

similar method: here we multiply the perimeter (length of boundary) of the cross-section by the length of the solid. Thus the area of the curved portion of the cylinder is length $\times$ circumference of circle, or $2\pi rl$. The area of the greenhouse, front and roof, excluding ends, is $(a + c) \times l$, since $(a + c)$ is the length of the perimeter of the portion considered.

Cone

The volume of a *cone* is $\frac{1}{3}\pi r^2 h$, where r and h are the radius of the base and the height of the cone. This is

perhaps best remembered as being *one-third of the volume of a cylinder on the same base and of the same height*. The curved surface area is πrl, and since the area of the base is πr^2, the total surface area of the cone is $\pi rl + \pi r^2$.

Sphere

The volume of a *sphere* (solid in the shape of a ball) is $\frac{4}{3}\pi r^3$, where r is its radius (not *diameter*); and its surface area is $4\pi r^2$.

The above formulae will be found sufficient to cover the areas and volumes of most ordinary figures. There is one geometrical theorem in addition which is frequently useful in finding dimensions of figures. This is called Pythagoras' Theorem (Pythagoras was an ancient Greek mathematician); it states that the sum of the areas obtained by squaring the sides *a* and *b* of a right-angled triangle (see figure) is equal to the area obtained by

squaring *c*, the side opposite to the right angle. Thus, $a^2 + b^2 = c^2$. If $a = 3$ ft., $b = 4$ ft., for example, *c* can be found, for

$$c^2 = a^2 + b^2 = 3^2 + 4^2 = 9 + 16 = 25 = 5^2;$$
$$\therefore \ c = 5 \text{ ft.}$$

Note that this theorem is true only for right-angled triangles, or triangles with a corner like that at P in the figure above. It is not true in the case of triangles like those in the figure of the trapezium on page 161.

Example 1. Find the area of glass needed for a greenhouse which is 50 ft. long, 8 ft. high at the front and 13 ft. at the back, and 12ft. deep. Each end is of glass, but each has a wooden door 6 ft. 6 in. by 2 ft. 6 in.

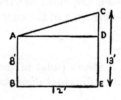

Since BE = 12 ft., AD = 12 ft.
Also　CD = 5 ft.
$\therefore$　AC^2 = 12^2 + 5^2 = 169.
$\therefore$　AC　　　　　　　 = 13 ft.
Now area of front = 8 × 50　　　　= 400 sq. ft.;
Area of top　　= 13 × 50　　　　= 650 sq. ft.;

Area of one end
     (with door) $= \frac{1}{2}(8 + 13) \times 12 = 126$ sq. ft.;
Area of door $= 6\frac{1}{2} \times 2\frac{1}{2}$ $= 16\frac{1}{4}$ sq. ft.;
$\therefore$ area of glass $= 400 + 650 + 2 \times 126 - 2 \times 16\frac{1}{4}$,
                       $= 1\,269\frac{1}{2}$ sq. ft.

Example 2. Find the volume of a memorial hall which
is circular and surmounted by a hemispherical dome, if
the radius of the floor is 30 ft., and the height from the
floor to the lowest part of the dome is 40 ft.

The hall consists of a cylinder and half a sphere. The
radius of both cylinder and sphere is 30 ft., and the
length of the cylinder is 40 ft.

Thus the volume is $\pi^2 h + \frac{2}{3}\pi r^3$,

$$= \pi \times 30^2 \times 40 + \tfrac{2}{3}\pi \times 30^3,$$
$$= 36\,000\pi + 18\,000\pi,$$
$$= 54\,000 \times 3{\cdot}142,$$
$$= 169\,668 \text{ cu. ft.}$$

EXERCISE 42

1. A triangular area is cut off from the corner of a square field,
the lengths of the sides at right-angles being 38 yd. and 23 yd.
Find the area cut off, and the decrease in the length of fencing
necessary for the field.

2. A house has a gable end; the lengths of the sides of the
triangle forming the gable are 22 ft., 22 ft. and 28 ft. Find the
area of the gable. (Divide the triangle into two identical halves
by drawing a vertical line from the apex of the gable, and find the
height by Pythagoras' Theorem.)

3. A railway cutting is 180 yd. long, 34 ft. deep, 26 ft. wide at
the bottom and 42 ft. at the top. Find the number of cubic yards
of earth excavated in making it.

4. A plot of ground has four points A, B, C, D at its corners.
B is 30 yd. due east of A, D is 20 yd. south-west of A, and C is due
east of D and also due south of B. Find the area of the plot and
the length of fence required to enclose it.

5. A roundabout on an arterial road is 30 yd. across. What
is its area?

6. The frontage of a crescent of houses is in the form of a semicircle. If the direct distance from one end of the crescent to the other is 187 yd., find the length of frontage.

7. Find the volume of a cocoa-tin, $4\frac{1}{2}$ in. high and $2\frac{3}{8}$ in. across.

8. Find the weight of 35 yd. of steel piping, $\frac{1}{8}$ in. thick, external diameter $2\frac{1}{4}$ in. 1 cu. in. of steel weighs 0·238 lb.

9. Find the weight of a round steel bar 10 ft. long and $2\frac{3}{8}$ in. thick.

10. Find the cubic capacity of a building on a rectangular foundation 15 ft. by 25 ft., 30 ft. high to the eaves, with two gable ends on the shorter sides, height of gables being 9 ft.

11. Find the area of material needed to form the curved surface of a loud-speaker cone of radius 8 in. and depth (i.e., "height" of cone) $3\frac{1}{2}$ in.

12. A rubber ball has diameter 6 in. If the rubber is $\frac{1}{4}$ in. thick, find the volume of rubber. (The answer is found by subtracting from the total volume of the ball the volume of the sphere formed by the space inside the ball; the diameter of the inner sphere is 6 in. $- 2 \times \frac{1}{4}$ in. $= 5\frac{1}{2}$ in.)

CHAPTER TWENTY-THREE

BUSINESS MATHEMATICS

INTEREST is money paid for the use of money. The money lent is called the *Principal*. The sum of the Principal and its Interest for any length of time is called the *Amount*. The money paid for the use of the Principal expressed as a percentage is called the *rate*, and since this is so much per £100 per year, it is called the *rate per cent. per annum*.

There are two kinds of interest: (1) *Simple*; (2) *Compound*.

When the interest is paid yearly, or at any rate periodically, and not added to the principal, it is called *Simple*. When the interest is added to the principal and so accumulates over a period, it is called *Compound*.

Simple Interest

To calculate simple interest we use the following formula:

Simple Interest
$$= \frac{\text{Principal} \times \text{Rate per cent.} \times \text{Number of Years}}{100}.$$

This is written as

$$I = \frac{PRN}{100} \text{ where } \begin{cases} P = \text{Principal} \\ R = \text{Rate per cent} \\ N = \text{Number of years.} \end{cases}$$

Example 1. Find Simple Interest on £500 for 84 days at $6\frac{1}{2}\%$ per annum.

$$\text{Interest} = \frac{84}{365} \times \frac{6\frac{1}{2}}{100} \text{ of } £500$$

$$= \frac{84}{365} \times \frac{\overset{42}{13}}{\underset{2}{200}} \times \overset{5}{£500}$$

$$= £\frac{546}{\underset{73}{73}}$$

$$= £7 \text{ 9s. 7d.}$$

Example 2. Find the Simple Interest on £3 695 15s. for 1 year and 8 months at $4\frac{1}{2}\%$ per annum.

Simple Interest $= 1\frac{2}{3} \times 4\frac{1}{2} \times £3$ 695 15s. $\div$ 100.

$$= \frac{5}{\underset{3}{3}} \times \frac{\overset{3}{9}}{2} \times \frac{1}{\underset{20}{100}} \times £3 \text{ 695 15s.}$$

$$= \frac{3}{40} \times £3 \text{ 695 15s.}$$

$$= 3 \times £92 \text{ 7s. } 10\frac{1}{2}\text{d.}$$

$$= £277 \text{ 3s. } 7\frac{1}{2}\text{d.}$$

Example 3. Find Simple Interest on £5 006 13s. 4d. for $2\frac{3}{4}$ years at $3\frac{1}{4}\%$.

Simple Interest $= £5$ 006 13s. 4d. $\times \frac{13}{4} \times \frac{1}{100} \times \frac{11}{4}$

$$= (£312 \text{ 18s. 4d. } \div 100) \times 13 \times 11$$

258

700

$$= £3 \text{ 2s. 7d.} \times 13 \times 11$$

$$= £40 \text{ 13s. 7d.} \times 11$$

$$= £447 \text{ 9s. 5d.}$$

In the above example, the principal was first divided by 4, the result divided again by 4, and this last result, viz., £312 18s. 4d. divided by 100, in the following manner: 100 goes 3 times into 312 and remainder 12. Mentally reduce 12 to shillings, adding in 18s. This gives 258s., which for convenience we place beneath 312. 100 goes 2 times into 258, and there is a remainder 58, which we reduce to pence, adding in 4, etc.

The result, £3 2s. 7d., we multiply *first* by 13 and then by 11, as it is easier to multiply 13 times £3 2s. 7d. by 11 than 11 times £3 2s. 7d. by 13.

N.B. When the time during which the interest is to be calculated is from one given day to another, *one only* of these days is reckoned.

Transformation of Formulae

Since Interest = (Principal × Rate per cent. × number of years) ÷ 100, that is $I = \dfrac{P \times R \times N}{100}$; or, what is the same thing,

$$\frac{P \times R \times N}{100} = I,$$

then it follows that—

$$P = I \div \left(\frac{R \times N}{100}\right);$$

$$R = I \div \left(\frac{P \times N}{100}\right);$$

$$N = I \div \left(\frac{P \times R}{100}\right);$$

or expressing these three facts in fractional form—

$$(1) \quad P = \frac{100 \times I}{R \times N};$$

$$(2) \quad R = \frac{100 \times I}{P \times N};$$

$$(3) \quad N = \frac{100 \times I}{P \times R}.$$

Example 4. In what time will a sum of £1 275 amount to £1 500 at $3\frac{1}{2}$% simple interest?

$$N = \frac{100 \times I}{P \times R}$$
$$= \frac{100 \times (1\ 500 - 1\ 275)}{1\ 275 \times 3\frac{1}{2}}$$
$$= \frac{100 \times \overset{\overset{3}{15}}{225} \times 2}{\underset{\underset{17}{85}}{1275} \times 7}$$
$$= \frac{600}{119}$$
$$= 5\frac{5}{119} \text{ years,}$$
$$= 5 \text{ years } 15 \text{ days.}$$

Example 5. What principal will amount to £1 600 at the end of 10 years at 5%?

Here the interest is not known, so that the formula $P = \dfrac{100 \times I}{R \times N}$ contains two unknowns, viz., P and I. But I = Amount − P;

$$\therefore P = \frac{100 \times (\text{Amount} - P)}{5 \times 10}$$
$$= \frac{100 \times 1\ 600 - 100P}{5 \times 10}$$
$$= \frac{160\ 000 - 100P}{50}$$
$$= 3\ 200 - 2P.$$

Add 2P to both sides;
$$\therefore 3P = 3\ 200;$$
$$\therefore \quad P = £1\ 066\tfrac{2}{3}.$$

EXERCISE 43

1. Find the simple interest of £183 6s. 8d. for $5\frac{2}{3}$ years at $4\frac{1}{2}$%.

2. Find the simple interest and amount of £37 1s. $11\frac{3}{4}$d. in $3\frac{1}{5}$ years at $6\frac{1}{4}$%.

3. Find the simple interest on £326 for 15 years at $4\frac{1}{2}$%.

4. Find the simple interest on £750 12s. 6d. for 1 year and 16 days at $2\frac{1}{2}$%.

5. Find the amount of £315 3s. 4d. in 2 years 2 months and 2 days at $1\frac{1}{2}$%. (365 days or 12 months = 1 year.)

6. Find the simple interest on £2 000 for 292 days at $3\frac{4}{5}$%. (Notice 73 days = $\frac{1}{5}$ year; 146 days = $\frac{2}{5}$; 219 days = $\frac{3}{5}$; 292 days = $\frac{4}{5}$.)

7. Find the simple interest on £370 11s. for 264 days at $2\frac{1}{2}$%. (Try a device similar to those in the last two worked examples.)

8. Find the simple interest and amount of £2 910 6s. 11d. in 79 days at $2\frac{3}{4}$%.

9. Find the simple interest on £815 5s. 7d. from 4th March to 4th August at $2\frac{1}{2}$% per annum.

10. Find the simple interest and amount of £1 890 10s. from 4th April, 1960, to 3rd September, 1961, at 5% per annum.

11. In what time will £5 027 10s. amount to £5 593 1s. $10\frac{1}{2}$d. at $2\frac{1}{2}$% per annum simple interest?

12. What sum of money will require to be invested at 4% in order to yield a person an annual income of £30?

13. At what rate per cent. simple interest will £183 6s. 8d. amount to £230 1s. 8d. in $5\frac{2}{3}$ years?

14. A person drew in all £16 10s. 6d. of interest on a sum of money that had lain in the bank for 7 months. During this time the rate of interest paid by the bank was $2\frac{1}{2}$% per annum. What was the sum of money?

15. The interest on £300 from 2nd June to 20th September is £2 5s. $2\frac{1}{2}$d.; at what rate is it calculated?

16. If $\frac{1}{4}$d. be the interest on 1s. for a calendar month, what is he rate per cent. per annum?

17. When a rate of interest is increased from 4 to $4\frac{1}{4}$%, the interest per annum is increased by 14s. 7d. What is the principal?

Compound Interest

First, if we want to know the interest for each year in £ s. d. as well as the total interest.

Example 6. Find the Compound Interest on £5 050 for 3 years at 4% per annum.

$$£5\ 050$$
$$4$$

		100)20 200		
Interest for first year	=	£2 02		
		£5 050		
Amount for first year	=	£5 252		
		4		
		100)21 008		
Interest for second year	=	£210	1	7·2
		5 252		
Amount for second year	=	£5 462	1	7·2
		4		
		100)21 848	6	4·8
Interest for third year	=	£218	9	8
∴ total interest		£630	11	3

Second (the more common form of the problem), if we want to know the *total* interest.

Example 7. (*The shortest and best method.*)

	£5 050
(1)	202·00
	5 252
(2)	210·08
	5 462·08
(3)	218·483 2
	5 680·563 2
(4)	£630·563 2
	2 0
	11·264 0
	1 2
	3·168

(1), (2) and (3) are the results of multiplying by 4 and dividing by 100; that is, we multiply by 4 and at the same time place each digit of the product two places to the right. (4)—the total interest—is got by subtracting first principal of £5 050 from the last amount £5 680·563 2.

Sometimes the interest is supposed to be due half-yearly or quarterly. In the former case, 2 years will be reckoned as four periods; and the interest calculated on each period will, of course, be at *half* the given rate.

Example 8. Find the compound interest on £250 for 1½ years at 2%, payable half-yearly. (Here there are 3 periods.)

		250
(1) First half-year's interest		2·5
		———
		252·5
(2) Second half-year's interest		2·525
		———
		255·025
(3) Third half-year's interest		2·550 25
		———
(4)		257·575 25
∴ com. int. = (4) − 250 =		£7·575 25
		20
		———
		11·505 00
		12
		———
		6·060

i.e., compound interest = £7 11s. 6d.

When the rate is fractional it is better to use the following method:

Example 9.   Find   the   Compound   Interest   on
£3 250 10s. 6d. for 2½ years at 2¼% per annum.

$$
\begin{array}{r}
12)6. \\
20)10\cdot5 \\
£3\ 250\cdot525
\end{array}
$$

$$2\tfrac{1}{4}\% = \begin{cases} 2\% = \tfrac{2}{100} & 65\cdot010\ 5\,|\,0 \\ \tfrac{1}{4}\% = \tfrac{1}{8}\ \text{of}\ 2\% & 8\cdot126\ 3\,|\,125 \end{cases}$$

$$\phantom{2\tfrac{1}{4}\%} \quad\quad 3\ 323\cdot661\ 8\,|\,125 \quad \text{First   year's}$$

$$2\tfrac{1}{4}\%\ \text{as before} = \begin{cases} 66\cdot473\ 2\,|\,36 \\ 8\cdot309\ 1\,|\,54 \end{cases} \quad \text{amount.}$$

$$ \quad\quad 3\ 398\cdot444\ 2\,|\,02 \quad \text{Second   year's}$$

$$\begin{matrix}\text{Half-year's} \\ \text{rate}\end{matrix} = 1\tfrac{1}{8}\% = \begin{cases} 1\% = \tfrac{1}{100} & 33\cdot984\ 4\,|\,42 \\ \tfrac{1}{8}\% = \tfrac{1}{8}\ \text{of}\ 1\% & 4\cdot248\ 0\,|\,55 \end{cases} \quad \text{amount.}$$

$$ \quad\quad \begin{array}{r} 3\ 436\cdot676\ 6\,|\,99 \\ 3\ 250\cdot525 \end{array} \quad \begin{matrix}\text{Half-year's} \\ \text{amount.}\end{matrix}$$

$$\therefore \text{ compound interest} = £186\cdot151\ 6$$

$$
\begin{array}{r}
20 \\
\hline
\text{s.}\ \ 3\cdot032\ 0 \\
12 \\
\hline
\text{d.}\ \ 0\cdot384\ 0
\end{array}
$$

$$\therefore \text{ compound interest} = £186\ 3\text{s. (approx.).}$$

Example 10.   A man saves £40 each year and invests it
at the end of the year at 4% compound interest; find the
amount of his savings, correct to the nearest penny, at
the end of the fourth year.

$$
\begin{array}{ll}
& £40 \qquad\qquad\ \text{Amount at end of first year.} \\
4\% = \tfrac{4}{100} = & \underline{6\cdot60} \\
& 41\cdot6 \\
& \underline{40} \\
& 81\cdot6 \qquad\qquad \text{Amount at end of second year.} \\
4\% = \tfrac{4}{100} = & 3\cdot264 \\
& 84\cdot864 \\
& \underline{40} \\
& 124\cdot864 \qquad\quad \text{Amount at end of third year.}
\end{array}
$$

$$4\% = \tfrac{4}{100} = \quad \underline{4 \cdot 994\ 56}$$

$$129 \cdot 858\ 56$$
$$40$$

$$\overline{169 \cdot 858\ 5} \quad \text{Amount at end of fourth year.}$$
$$20$$

$$\overline{17 \cdot 170\ 0}$$
$$12$$

$$\overline{2 \cdot 04} \qquad \therefore \text{ amount} = \pounds 169 \text{ 17s. 2d.}$$

The calculation by the methods given above of compound interest for longer periods than three or four years becomes very laborious. In such cases it is usual to use the formula

$$A_n = P\left(1 + \frac{r}{100}\right)^n$$

where n = number of years
$\quad\quad\quad\quad A_n$ = Amount after n years
$\quad\quad\quad\quad$ P = Principal
$\quad\quad\quad\quad r$ = rate

or the following table

AMOUNT OF £1 AT COMPOUND INTEREST

No. of Yrs.	2½%	3%	3½%	4%	4½%	5%
1	1·025 00	1·030 00	1·035 00	1·040 00	1·045 00	1·050 00
2	1·050 62	1·060 90	1·071 22	1·081 60	1·092 03	1·102 50
3	1·076 89	1·092 73	1·108 72	1·124 86	1·141 17	1·157 63
4	1·103 81	1·125 51	1·147 52	1·169 86	1·192 52	1·215 51
5	1·131 41	1·159 27	1·187 69	1·216 65	1·246 18	1·276 28
10	1·280 08	1·343 92	1·410 60	1·480 24	1·552 97	1·628 89
15	1·448 30	1·557 97	1·675 35	1·800 94	1·935 28	2·078 93
20	1·638 62	1·806 11	1·989 79	2·191 12	2·411 71	2·653 30
25	1·853 94	2·093 78	2·363 24	2·665 84	3·005 43	3·386 35

By combining two of these figures, this table covers the years not actually specified. The method is indicated in Example 14 of the next Exercise.

EXERCISE 44

1. Find the compound interest on £500 for 2 years at 2% per annum.

2. Find the compound interest on £625 10s. 6d. for 2½ years at 3% per annum.

3. Find the compound interest on £420 for 2½ years at 4% per annum, the interest being payable half-yearly.

4. Find what £30 will amount to in 3½ years at 4% per annum compound interest.

5. Find the compound interest on £3 600, accumulated during 3½ years at 2½% per annum.

6. A man invests in a business £400, and allows it to accumulate for 2 years at 2¾%. What amount is due him at the end of the 2 years?

7. Find to the nearest penny the compound interest on £2 743 17s. 6d. for 3 years at 3½%. (Note, 17s. 6d. = £⅞ = £0·875.)

8. Find, without unnecessary calculation, the amount to the nearest penny at the end of 2 years of £1 248 invested at 4% per annum compound interest, payable half-yearly.

9. A person borrows £200, and at the end of each year pays £50 to reduce the principal and pay interest at 5%. How much will he remain in debt at the end of 2 years?

10. Find the compound interest on £3 600 accumulated during 3½ years at 2½% per annum. If for the last half-year the interest be reduced to 1⅝% per annum, what will be the difference in the whole amount?

(*For the following use the compound interest formula or table.*)

11. Find the amount of £250 after 10 years at 3½% compound interest.

12. Find the compound interest on £133 15s. for 25 years at 4½%.

13. Find the compound interest on £2 716 for 5 years at 2½%.

14. Find the amount of £364 at 5% compound interest after (*a*) 13 years, (*b*) 19 years.

(The amount of £1 after 13 years is £1·628 89 × 1·157 63, combining the values in the table for 10 years and 3 years.)

Profit and Loss

An application of percentages (see Chapter 19) is in problems on Profit and Loss. There is little new to be learned; the principle at the bottom of the solution of every problem is the same as you have met before.

Before working an example of each case likely to be

met with in actual practice, we would draw attention to the following points:

1. A profit or loss per cent. means that the percentage is calculated *on the cost price*. Thus, suppose there is a profit of 10% on the sale of an article, the selling price = (100 + 10)% = 110% (of cost price).

If there is a loss of 10%, then selling price = (100 − 10)% = 90% (of cost price).

2. In a complicated transaction, where an article passes through the hands of several persons before it reaches the consumer, each person (manufacturer, merchant, etc.) calculates the profit or loss as a percentage, not on the original cost price, but *on his own cost price*.

Example 11. What is the profit per cent. gained by selling at £15 an article which cost £12?

Gain on £12 is £3;

that is, profit = $\frac{3}{12}$ = $\frac{1}{4}$ of cost price.

Now, on the supposition that cost price is £100, profit per cent. must = $\frac{1}{4}$ of 100 = 25.

Example 12. I bought an article for 13s., and sold it for 12s. 6d.; what was my loss per cent.?

Loss on 13s. = 6d.;

$$\text{that is, loss} = \frac{6d.}{13s.} \text{ of cost price}$$
$$= \tfrac{1}{26} \text{ of cost price;}$$
$$\therefore \text{ loss per cent.} = \tfrac{1}{26} \text{ of 100}$$
$$= 3\tfrac{11}{13}.$$

Example 13. A grocer bought a cask of sugar containing 2½ cwt. at 4½d. per lb. Allowing 2½% for waste, what must he sell it at per lb. in order to gain not less than 25%?

$$\text{Cost of } 2\tfrac{1}{2} \text{ cwt.} = 2\tfrac{1}{2} \times 112 \times 4\tfrac{1}{2} \text{ pence}$$

$$= \frac{5}{2} \times \overset{7}{\underset{}{112}} \times \frac{\overset{3}{9}}{2} \times \frac{\overset{1}{1}}{240} \text{ pounds}$$

$$= \pounds\frac{21}{4}$$

$$= \pounds 5 \text{ 5s.}$$

Selling price must be $\pounds 5$ 5s. + 25% of $\pounds 5$ 5s.

$$= \pounds 5 \text{ 5s.} + \tfrac{1}{4} \text{ of } \pounds 5 \text{ 5s.}$$

$$= \pounds 5 \text{ 5s.} + \pounds 1 \text{ 6s. 3d.}$$

$$= \pounds 6 \text{ 11s. 3d.}$$

$2\tfrac{1}{2}$ cwt. $- 2\tfrac{1}{2}\%$ of $2\tfrac{1}{2}$ cwt. $= (2\tfrac{1}{2} - \tfrac{1}{40} \text{ of } 2\tfrac{1}{2})$ cwt.

$$= (2\tfrac{1}{2} - \tfrac{1}{16}) \text{ cwt.}$$

$$= 2\tfrac{7}{16} \text{ cwt.};$$

∴ price per lb. must be—

$$= \frac{\pounds 6 \text{ 11s. 3d.}}{2\tfrac{7}{16} \times 112}$$

$$= \frac{\pounds 6 \text{ 11s. 3d.}}{\underset{16}{39} \times \overset{7}{112}}$$

$$= \frac{\pounds 6 \text{ 11s. 3d.}}{273}$$

$$= \frac{1\,575}{273} \text{ pence}$$

$$= 6\text{d. (nearly).}$$

Example 14. One bookseller allows 2d. in the shilling discount, and an additional 5% on the remaining price; another simply allows 20% on the published price of the books. Find which terms are the better, and the difference on $\pounds 100$ worth of books (published price).

First bookseller allows $\frac{2}{12}$ or $\frac{1}{6}$ of published price

$$+ \frac{5}{100} \text{ of } \frac{5}{6} \text{ of published price}$$
$$= \frac{1}{6} + \frac{1}{24} = \frac{5}{24} \text{ in all, } = \frac{5}{24} \text{ of } 100 = 20\frac{5}{6}.$$

Second bookseller allows 20%, therefore first terms are better by $\frac{5}{6}$%, that is, the saving on £100 worth of books would be £$\frac{5}{6}$ or 16s. 8d.

Example 15. A merchant mixes wines at 15s., 20s. and 25s. a gallon respectively in the proportion of 2, 3, 1, and sells the mixture at 20s. per gallon. What is his gain or loss per cent.?

2 gall. at 15s.	= 30s.
3 gall. at 20s.	= 60s.
1 gall. at 25s.	= 25s.
∴ 6 gall. of mixture cost	115s;
∴ 1 gall. cost	19$\frac{1}{6}$s.;
∴ gain on 1 gall. of mixture	= $\frac{5}{6}$s.
	= 10d.
∴ gain per cent.	= $\dfrac{10\text{d.}}{19\frac{1}{6}\text{s.}}$ of 100
	= $\frac{5}{6} \times \dfrac{6}{\underset{23}{115}} \times 100$
	= $4\frac{8}{23}$.

EXERCISE 45

1. A man buys an article for 5d. and sells it for 6d. What is his gain per cent.?

2. A merchant buys 640 oranges for 48s. The cost of packing is 6% extra, and the cost of carriage is 10s. 3% of the oranges go bad. How must he sell the oranges so as to gain 16s. on every hundred sold?

3. If 48 gall. of spirit at 12s. per gall., 2$\frac{2}{3}$ gall. at 10s. 6d. and 19$\frac{1}{4}$ gall. at 1s. 4d. be mixed with 19$\frac{5}{6}$ gall. of water, and the mixture sold at 7s. 10$\frac{1}{4}$d. per gall., what is the gain per cent?

4. A bookseller buys a certain class of books at 4s. each. What must he charge for each book so as to make a profit of 15%?

5. A merchant bought goods at the rate of £7 10s. per cwt., and retails them at 2s. per lb. The cost of carriage of the goods was 3s. per cwt., and 2% of them was lost through waste, etc. Does the retail price make a profit or loss? And by how much?

6. An electric toaster uses 1 unit of electricity in 2½ hr. It is used for 10 min. each morning. The cost of 1 unit is either ½d. (power rate) or 2½d. (light rate). The cost of installing a special power plug to make the cheaper rate possible is £1 1s. What is the gain, expressed as a percentage of the cost of electricity at the light rate, over a period of 8 years, of installing the special plug?

7. A housekeeper needs 48 eggs a month for cooking purposes. She pickles eggs in June, bought at 4s. a dozen, for use during the months Oct. to March. The cost of pickling is 15s. If she bought the eggs as she needed them the prices would be: in Oct. 4s. 9d. per doz., in Nov. 5s., in Dec. 5s. 3d., in Jan. and Feb. 5s. 6d., in March 5s. 3d. Express her profit as a percentage of what she might have spent.

8. A dealer bought some stock for £158 6s. 8d. He sold a quarter of it for £45 10s. 5d. and the remainder for £142 10s. Find his gain per cent. on the two portions separately and on the whole transaction.

ANSWERS

EXERCISE 1, page 17

1. (a) 29 (b) 176 (c) 71.
2. (a) 73 (b) 1 600 (c) 1 446.
3. (a) 83 (b) 128 (c) 597.
4. (a) 69 (b) 86 (c) 237.
5. (a) 418 (b) 735 (c) 11 826.
6. (a) 76 (b) 281 (c) 56.
7. 910.
8. 399.
9. 4, 9, 16, 25, 36, 49, 64, 81, 100, 121, 144, 169, 196, 225, 256, 289, 324, 361, 400. (It is useful to know these by heart.)
10. 5, 2, 4, 9, 12; 15, 3, 7, 10, 13; 19, 14, 17, 1, 11; 20, 18, 6, 8. (It is useful to know these by heart.)

EXERCISE 2, page 26

1. $2a$.
2. $-17b$.
3. $-6x$.
4. $-6d$.
5. $-12x^2$.
6. $-9xy$.
7. $-7x^2y$.
8. $12a + 8c + d$.
9. $14xy + 5b$.
10. $13a^2 + 3ab$.
11. (a) $-3cx - cy + yz$; (b) 3.
12. (a) $ax + bx - 7cx$; (b) -126.
13. $4x - 2\frac{3}{12}xy - \frac{1}{2}y$.
14. $\frac{1}{4}a^3 - 4a^2b + b^3$.
15. $12a + \frac{7}{3}c$.

EXERCISE 3, page 29

1. $-9a - c$.
2. $-12x + 3y - 3z$.
3. $-9ab + xy + z$.
4. $-2x^2$.
5. $-8xy - 2yz + 2xz$.
6. $-8p - 2q + r$.
7. $2p - q + 2r - s$.
8. $2ab + bc$.
9. $-5pq + 4qr - 3s$.
10. $-8x^2 + 6y^2 + 2z^2$.
11. $\frac{3}{2}x^2 + y^2 - \frac{1}{4}z^2$.
12. $\frac{7}{12}ab + \frac{5}{2}bc - \frac{1}{4}cd$.

EXERCISE 4, page 33

1. $2a^3b^3c^4$.
2. $-2x^4y^5z$.
3. $x^3 + x^2y$.
4. $x^4 + 2x^3y + x^2y^2$.
5. $a^2 + 2ab + b^2 + ac + bc$.
6. $a^3 + 3a^2b + 3ab^2 + b^3$.
7. $3x^4 - x^2y^2 + 3x^2y - y^3$.
8. $a^3 - a^2b - ab^2 - a^2c + b^2c + b^3$.

9. $x^3 + x^2y - xy^2 - y^3$. 13. $\frac{1}{8}x^4 - \frac{1}{8}y^4$.

10. $x^3 - x^2y - xy^2 + y^3$. 14. $\frac{1}{2}xy^3 - \frac{1}{2}xy^2z + \frac{1}{2}xyz^2 - \frac{1}{2}xz^3$.

11. $a^4 - 2a^2b^2 + b^4$. 15. $x^6 - y^6$.

12. $2a^2 - 3ab + 3a - 2b^2 - b + 1$.

Exercise 5, page 36

1. $3a$.

2. $-4b$.

3. $-4xz$.

4. $a + b$.

5. $a + b$.

6. $a - b$.

7. $a^2 + ab + b^2$.

8. $a^2 - ab + b^2$.

9. $a - b + \dfrac{2b^2}{a - b}$.

10. $a^2 - 3ax + x^2$.

11. $2x^2 + xy + 3y^2$.

12. $x^4 + ax^3 - a^3x - a^4$.

13. $x^2 - a^2$.

14. $x^2 - 2xy + y^2$.

15. $p^3 - 3p^2q + 3pq^2 - q^3$.

Exercise 6, page 40

1. 2.

2. 5.

3. 2.

4. 2.

5. 51.

6. 37.

Exercise 7, page 41

1. 60.

2. 1 260.

3. 144.

4. 1 260.

5. 78.

6. 34 944.

Exercise 8, page 47

1. 44.

2. 84.

3. 13.

4. 25.

5. 32.

6. 252.

7. 219.

8. $36 + 2 = 38$.

9. A $= 30 \div 5 = 6$.

10. P $= 48 \div 16 = 3$.

11. P $= 36 \div 6 = 6$.

12. P $= 84 \div 3 = 28$.

13. 286 320; 626 325; 876 855; 1 288 440.

14. 4 773 690; 20 049 498; 34 370 568.

15. 9 427 930; 94 279 300; 942 793 000; 9 427 930 000.

16. 96 499; 103 922; 111 345; 118 768; 126 191; 133 614; 141 037.

17. 2 239 475; 6 718 425; 11 197 375.

18. 1 230, remainder 6; 1 025, remainder 6; 769; 256, remainder 24.

19. 5 892, remainder 1; 4 285, remainder 3; 3 491, remainder 16; 872, remainder 97.

20. 9 845, remainder 6; 984, remainder 56; 98, remainder 456; 9, remainder 8 456.

Exercise 9, page 51

1. $a + b - c - d.$
2. $2a - 2b - 3c + 3d.$
3. $-a + b - c + d.$
4. $-2a + 2b + c - d.$
5. $2a + b + c.$
6. $\frac{1}{2}x.$
7. $-q + r + s.$
8. $4x - 2y.$
9. $4q + 2r - 2s.$
10. $-2ab + 2cd + 2ef.$
11. $-(p + q) - (r - s).$
12. $(2p - q) + (r - s).$
13. $-(xy + yz) - (p + 2q) + (r - s).$
14. $(6ab - 2bc) - (3cd + 4de) - (5ef - 6fg).$
15. $-(p - q) + (2r - s) - (t - w).$
16. $-2(q + 2q) - (r - s) - 2(t + w).$

Exercise 10, page 52

1. $17.$
2. $77.$
3. $300.$
4. $-144.$
5. $2.$
6. $7\frac{1}{3}.$
7. $\frac{25}{64}.$
8. $-6\,300.$
9. $15\,750.$
10. $5\,835\frac{29}{32}.$

Exercise 11, page 54

1. $101.$
2. $0.$
3. $\frac{1}{96}.$
4. $26\frac{1}{2}.$
5. $11.$
6. $-\frac{5}{48}.$
7. $64\frac{1}{24}.$
8. $1\frac{1}{24}.$
9. $\frac{5}{6}.$
10. $\frac{11}{12}.$

Exercise 12, page 59

1. $\frac{9}{10}, \frac{1}{2}, \frac{1}{3}, \frac{13}{19}.$
2. $0, \frac{7}{12}, \frac{1}{72}.$
3. $£1\frac{191}{240}.$
4. $4\frac{197}{240}$ tons.
5. $\frac{12}{35}.$
6. $\frac{4}{9}, \frac{12}{13}.$
7. $\frac{11}{45}.$
8. $\frac{17}{80}.$
9. $\frac{8}{9}, \frac{7}{8}, \frac{2}{3}, \frac{6}{10}, \frac{4}{7}, \frac{5}{9}.$
10. $8\frac{4}{7}$ min.
11. $17\frac{1}{7}$ hr.
12. $\frac{10}{41}, \frac{31}{41}.$

Exercise 13, page 61

1. $\frac{5}{2} = 2\frac{1}{2}.$
2. $\frac{3}{7}.$
3. $\frac{10}{3} = 3\frac{1}{3}.$
4. $2.$
5. $\frac{9}{4} = 2\frac{1}{4}.$
6. $\frac{4}{7}.$
7. $\frac{45}{7} = 6\frac{3}{7}.$
8. $3.$
9. $£10.$
10. 5 fur.
11. $7 \times \frac{1}{2}$ yd. $= \frac{7}{2} = 3\frac{1}{2}$ yd.
12. $\frac{18}{5}$ ton $= 3\frac{3}{5}$ tons.
13. $\frac{1}{4}.$
14. $\frac{1}{25}.$
15. $\frac{2}{25}.$
16. $\frac{15}{28}.$
17. $\frac{3}{8}$ yd.
18. $\frac{10}{48}$ mile or $\frac{5}{24}$ mile.

19. $\frac{3}{4}$ of $\frac{5}{2} = \frac{15}{8} = 1\frac{7}{8}$.   20. $\frac{5}{8}$ of $\frac{15}{2} = \frac{75}{16} = 4\frac{11}{61}$ tons.
21. $\frac{3}{5} \times \frac{81}{2} = \frac{243}{10} = 24\frac{3}{10}$ sq. yd.
22. $\frac{7}{8} \times 35\frac{1}{2} = \frac{7}{8} \times \frac{71}{2} = \frac{497}{16} = £31\frac{1}{16}$.
23. $\frac{9}{10} \times \frac{141}{4} = \frac{1269}{40} = 31\frac{29}{40}$ acres.
24. $\frac{4}{7} \times \frac{7}{2} = 2$ guineas.

EXERCISE 14, page 62

1. Each part $= \frac{5}{24}$.   7. $\frac{64}{3} = 21\frac{1}{3}$.
2. $\frac{5}{42}$.   8. $\frac{20}{21}$.
3. $\frac{4}{75}$.   9. $\frac{15}{56}$.
4. $\frac{8}{72} = \frac{1}{9}$.   10. $\frac{5}{24}$.
5. $\frac{13}{70}$.   11. $60 \times \frac{4}{3} = 80$.
6. 50.
12. $1260 \times \frac{2}{7} = 360 + 1 = 361$ posts.
13. 68 and $\frac{1}{2}$ yd. over.   14. 136 times and $\frac{2}{3}$ of a time.

EXERCISE 15, page 65

1. $\frac{x}{4y}, \frac{7x}{y}, \frac{x^3}{2y^3}$.

2. $\frac{ac}{b}, ce, \frac{p^2}{q}$.

3. $\frac{3p}{qr}, \frac{18mn}{l}, \frac{4s^2}{v^2}$.

4. $\frac{3x + 2x}{6} = \frac{5x}{6}$.

5. $\frac{115x}{24}$.

6. $\frac{3m - 2n}{24}$.

7. $\frac{pqr + 2pq}{r^2} = \frac{pq(r + 2)}{r^2}$.

8. $\frac{8x + 4x - 3x}{24} = \frac{9x}{24} = \frac{3x}{8}$.

9. $\frac{37x}{60}$.

10. $\frac{-4a^2b^2}{9}$.

11. $\frac{84}{5}y^3$.

12. $\frac{27q}{2p^2}$.

13. $\frac{ab^3c}{mnpq}$.

14. $-\frac{1}{ab}$.

15. $\frac{9b^3x^2}{4p}$.

16. $-\frac{210a^3c}{b}$.

EXERCISE 16, page 68

1. 46·480.   6. 0·75.
2. 96·905 9.   7. 7·837 05.
3. 132·042.   8. 2·65.
4. 9 821·941 5.   9. 10·991.
5. 2 179·442 119.   10. 0·004 5

EXERCISE 17, page 72

1. 0·407.
2. 59·285.
3. 720·810 09.
4. 0·000 005 4.
5. 7 723·248 75.
6. 7.
7. 3·804 . . .
8. 18 200.
9. 4 330.
10. 0·010 01.
11. 1 650·94 . . .
12. 1000.
13. 0·000 35.
14. 2·67 . . .
15. 56 866 times, and a remainder of $\frac{10}{15}$ or $\frac{2}{3}$ of 0·015 = 0·01.
16. 131·25 ft.
17. 101·76 hr.
18. 135 pieces and $\frac{5}{12}$ of a piece = 0·05 in.

EXERCISE 18, page 79

1. $\frac{51}{163}$.
2. $2\frac{1}{2}$.
3. $\frac{1}{6}$.
4. $\frac{1525}{61952}$.
5. 0·458 3 (3 repeating).
6. 0·648 148 14 . . . where 481 repeats indefinitely.
7. 0·020 83 (3 repeating).
8. 0·023 80 . . . = 0·024 (nearly).
9. 12s. 2·1d.
10. $1\frac{1}{2}$d.
11. 0·353 125.
12. 5·875.
13. £57 19s. 10d. (nearly).
14. 0·004 464 . . .
15. 0·928 571 4 (285714 repeats indefinitely).
16. 0·698 . . . = 0·7 (practically.
17. $\frac{200}{441}$.
18. 3·175.
19. £40 1s. 3d.
20. $\frac{7}{25}$.
21. £20 3s. 8·9d.
22. £13·45 (3·25 + 9·45 + 0·75).
23. 5·354 16 (6 repeating).
24. 2s. 1·68d.
25. 78·187 7 . . .

EXERCISE 19, page 85

(Several answers in this Exercise are given to a much greater degree of accuracy than would be needed in practice.)

1. 240 498 in.
2. 27 669 yd.
3. 4 221 ft.
4. 26 482$\frac{1}{2}$ yd.
5. 30 900 lk.
6. 10 miles 1 fur. 9 ch. 2 yd. 1 ft.
7. 1 mile 1 ch. 11 yd.
8. 100 miles.
9. 2 fur. 4 ch. 10 yd.
10. 1 mile 8 ch. 2 ft. 3 in.
11. 94·096 m.
12. 7 176·881 m.
13. 98 997·583 m.
14. 10·059 4 Km.
15. 512·842 635 Km.
16. 924·274 948 Km.
17. 29 miles 5 fur. 7 ch. 2 yd.
18. 28 Km. 5 Hm. 8 Dm. 4 m.
19. 115·895 m.
20. 2 miles 1 621 yd. 2 ft. 6 in.; 1 623 yd. 2 ft. 2$\frac{1}{2}$ in. (approx.).

21. 823·04 m.
22. 0·288 . . . m.
23. 7 strips.
24. 1 045.
25. 557 miles 1 364 yd.

26. 500.
27. 0·914 4 m.
28. 0·393 7 in.
29. 4 419·905 m. 4·419 905 Km.
30. 541·860 8 miles.

Exercise 20, page 89

1. 2 000 000 cu. cm.
2. 10 000 sq. m.
3. 91·215 096 cu. m.
4. 54·234 433 cu. m.

5. 0·404 7 hectare.
6. 0·155 0 sq. in.
7. 163 87 cu. mm.

Exercise 21, page 91

(Several answers in this exercise will vary slightly according to the approximate equivalent used as the starting-point.)

1. 13 oz. 2·04 drams (approx.).
2. 65·34 cu. ft. (approx.).
3. 568¼.
4. (1) 2 571·43 francs.   (2) 104 064 francs.
5. 285 litres.
6. 229 francs.
7. 1·84 Hl.
8. 173 francs 54 centimes.
9. 2 620·86 Kg.
10. 62·4 lb. approx.
11. 4 lb. 11½ oz. approx.
12. The second, by 1 franc 25 centimes.

Exercise 22, page 94

1. 16; 21; 25.
2. 35; 36; 57.

3. 38; 84; 87.
4. 175; 130; 315.

Exercise 23, page 97

1. 139·1 yd.
2. 40·477 poles.
3. 100 yd.
4. 191 yd.
5. 453·27 . . . poles.
6. 40·166

7. 70 yd.
8. £130·153
9. 720 yd.
10. 17·46 ft.
11. 43·006 ft.
12. 220 yd.

Exercise 24, page 99

1. 6; 11; 12.
2. 8; 13; 14.
3. 15; 18; 17.

4. £2 15s. 1½d.
5. 10 ft.
6. 10 ft.

EXERCISE 25, page 103

1. $x = -1$.
2. $x = 4\frac{1}{3}$.
3. $x = 5$.
4. $x = -5\frac{1}{2}$.
5. $p = 2\frac{1}{4}$.
6. $x = 31$.
7. $x = \frac{4}{11}$.
8. $x = 6\frac{4}{7}$.
9. $x = 41\frac{2}{23}$.
10. $x = -\frac{26}{33}$.
11. $x = \frac{5}{41}$.
12. $x = 7\frac{6}{19}$.
13. $x = 17\frac{41}{47}$.
14. $x = -30$.
15. $x = -\frac{41}{17} = -2\frac{7}{17}$.
16. A $= 66$.
17. V $= 1706\frac{2}{3}$.
18. $s = 788 \cdot 9$.
19. $s = \frac{112}{55} = 2 \cdot 03 \ldots$
20. $a = \frac{589}{50} = 11 \cdot 78$.
21. $m = 9 \cdot 6$.
22. $v^2 = 1500$, $\therefore v = \sqrt{1500} = 38 \cdot 7$.
23. $w = \frac{3900}{11} = 354 \cdot 5\dot{4}$.
24. V $= 104$.
25. $f = 5 \cdot 6$.
26. I $= 30$.
27. P $= 857\frac{1}{7}$.
28. N $= \frac{55}{64}$.
29. R $= 2\frac{74}{203}$.
30. (1) A $= 1200$; (2) $h = 11\frac{1}{4}$.

EXERCISE 26, page 108

1. $72 - p$.
2. $p - q$.
3. $\frac{p}{3\frac{1}{2}} = \frac{2p}{7}$.
4. $\frac{350}{x}$ hr.
5. $(\frac{5}{2}p + 2q)$.
6. $(240x + 12y + z)$ pence.
7. $\frac{b}{c}$ hr.
8. $\frac{k}{q}$ miles per hour.
9. $\frac{240}{20} =$ number of scores; $\therefore$ 12 score at p pence each score cost $12p$ pence, $12p$ pence $= \frac{12p}{12}$ shillings $= p$ shillings.
10. $6p$ miles.

EXERCISE 27, page 108

1. 4 in. and 12 in.
2. £166 13s. 4d., £833 6s. 8d.
3. $28\frac{4}{5}$ ft.
4. $(2x + 124 - x = 177)$; $\therefore$ 53 florins 71 shillings.
5. A gets £210, B and C each get £70.
6. 10 lb.
7. C gets £14 13s. 4d., B gets £19 13s. 4d., A gets £25 13s. 4d.
8. In 6 hr.

EXERCISE 28, page 114

1. $x = 3, y = 1$.
2. $y = 2, x = 2$.
3. $p = -5, q = -7$.
4. $y = 6, x = 5$.

5. $y = -3$, $x = -7$.   7. $B = \frac{3}{5}$, $A = -\frac{27}{5}$.

6. $B = \frac{17}{7}$, $A = \frac{2}{7}$.

8. $a = \frac{55}{4}$, $c = -10$; $\therefore F = \frac{55}{4} B - 10$.

9. 23 and 17.

10. 1 lb. of sugar costs $3\frac{1}{2}$d.; 1 lb. of tea costs 3s.

11. Boy receives 12s. 6d., man receives £1 2s. 6d.

12. $a = \frac{4}{13}$, $b = \frac{21}{13}$.

13. $a = \frac{37}{104}$, $b = \frac{159}{13}$.

EXERCISE 29, page 117

1. $\frac{20}{21}$, or 20 : 21.   9. 1 760 : 1.

2. 201 : 481.   10. 2nd.

3. 151 : 40.   11. 1st.

4. 1 : 5.   12. 1st.

5. 92 160 : 1.   13. 1 : 3.

6. 9 : 1 210.   14. 27 : 13.

7. 1 : 40.   15. 22 : 7.

8. 18 : 77.   16. 20 : 17.

17. 1 117 : 12 000; 361 : 10 500; 34 267 : 216 000; 2 217 : 5 800.

EXERCISE 30, page 122

1. $10\frac{1}{2}$.   11. $6\frac{2}{3}$.   21. 6.

2. 16.   12. $1\frac{5}{8}$.   22. 9.

3. 45.   13. $1\frac{1}{2}$.   23. 8.

4. 432.   14. 9.   24. 15.

5. 21.   15. $2\frac{2}{3}$.   25. $\frac{1}{6}$.

6. 18.   16. 32.   26. $\frac{1}{4}$.

7. 32.   17. $5\frac{4}{9}$.   27. 12.

8. 10.   18. 147.   28. 14.

9. 8.   19. $\frac{1}{8}$.   29. 3.

10. 24.   20. 243.   30. $\frac{1}{12}$.

EXERCISE 31, page 125

1. 3 qr. $18\frac{1}{40}$ lb.   6. 62 ft. 5·2 in.

2. £41 4s. 6d.   7. 7 lb. $\frac{1}{2}$ oz. (nearly).

3. £84.   8. 4s. 5d. (nearly).

4. 3s. $2\frac{1}{4}$d. (nearly).   9. £148 3s.

5. 17·43 cu. ft.   10. 36 days.

EXERCISE 32, page 127

1. £27 14s. 2d.   6. £149 7s.

2. £11 0s. $9\frac{1}{4}$d.   7. Any length less than $87\frac{1}{2}$ yd.

3. £12.   8. £3 2s. 10d.

4. $60\frac{3}{5}$ yd.   9. (1) $1\frac{13}{32}$d.; (2) $1\frac{2}{25}$d.

5. 49 days ($49\frac{1}{51}$).   10. £4 4s. 4d.

EXERCISE 33, page 130

1. $7\frac{5}{7}$ days.
2. $6\frac{1}{4}$d.
3. $39\frac{3}{5}$ tons.
4. £1 5s. $4\frac{1}{2}$d.
5. £12 13s. 8d.

6. 45 min.
7. 293.
8. 16 hr. $17\frac{1}{7}$ min.
9. £100 14s. 1d.

EXERCISE 34, page 135

1. £15, £20, £25.
2. £46 11s. $5\frac{1}{4}$d., £93 2s. $10\frac{2}{7}$d., £186 5s. $8\frac{4}{7}$d.
3. 24 ft. and 26 ft.
4. £44 16s. 5d. (nearly).
5. £352 11s. ($10\frac{50}{59}$s.), £418 13s. ($12\frac{52}{59}$s.), £528 16s. ($16\frac{16}{69}$s.).
6. Actual $\begin{cases} £331 \text{ 7s. } 10\frac{38}{43}\text{d.} = £331 \text{ 7s. } 11\text{d.} \\ £77 \text{ 6s. } 6\frac{6}{43}\text{d.} = £77 \text{ 6s. } 6\text{d.} \\ £66 \text{ 5s. } 6\frac{42}{43}\text{d.} = £66 \text{ 5s. } 7\text{d.} \end{cases}$ Practical result.
   result
7. £275, £183 6s. 8d., £91 13s. 4d.
8. £9 15s. 8d. (nearly), £20 19s. 4d. (nearly).
9. $34\frac{2}{7}$ lb.; $5\frac{5}{7}$ lb., $11\frac{3}{7}$ lb., $2\frac{6}{7}$ lb., $5\frac{5}{7}$ lb.
10. Each child gets £12 1s. $10\frac{3}{4}$d.
    Each woman gets £36 5s. $8\frac{1}{4}$d. } (nearly).
    Each man gets £72 11s. $4\frac{1}{2}$d.
11. £33 8s. 1d.
    £25 1s. 1d. } (nearly).
    £20 0s. 10d.
12. 48·457 (approx.).
13. Housing: £179 8s. 4d.
    Health: £103 4s. 6d.
    Ditches: £185 2s. 11d.
    Administration: £272 4s. 3d.

EXERCISE 35, page 138

1. $24\frac{1}{2}$ miles.
2. 5·333 · · · = 5·$\dot{3}$ (3 repeating).
3. 740 (thousand).
4. 33·58 runs.
5. 48 miles.
6. £6 14s. 2d.
7. About 1 in 88.
8. £2 1s. $5\frac{4}{7}$d.
9. $10\frac{1}{2}$ m.p.h. (nearly).

10. 38·4.
11. 62·71 degrees.
12. 43·81 miles (nearly).
13. $1\frac{7}{11}$d.
14. $37\frac{1}{2}$ m.p.h.
15. 10 st. $2\frac{3}{4}$ lb.
16. £1 10s. 4d.

Exercise 36, page 141

1. $\frac{3}{5}$.
2. $\frac{3}{4}$.
3. $\frac{7}{20}$.
4. $\frac{2}{5}$.
5. $\frac{1}{12}$.

6. $\frac{2}{25}$.
7. $\frac{1}{40}$.
8. $\frac{11}{400}$.
9. $\frac{1}{80}$.
10. 1.

11. $\frac{3}{16}$.
12. $\frac{1}{250}$.
13. $\frac{1}{800}$.
14. $\frac{3}{40}$.
15. $1\frac{1}{2}$.

16. 50, $33\frac{1}{3}$, 25, 20, $16\frac{2}{3}$.
17. $66\frac{2}{3}$, 75, 90, $62\frac{1}{2}$, 60.
18. 40, $88\frac{8}{9}$, 80, $87\frac{1}{2}$, 50.

19. 75, 300, $2\frac{1}{2}$, 2, $37\frac{1}{2}$.
20. 6, 125, 120, 25, 45.

Exercise 37, page 142

1. (1) £3 12s.
   (2) £4 4s. 6d.
   (3) £3 10s. $10\frac{1}{2}$d.
   (4) £3 3s.
   (5) £98 15s. $4\frac{4}{5}$d.
   (6) 90 yd.
   (7) 10 cwt. $11\frac{1}{3}$ lb.
   (8) 88 yd.
   (9) $1\frac{1}{2}$ hr.
   (10) 80 yd.

2. (1) £15.
   (2) £7 10s.
   (3) £24 7s. 6d.
   (4) £1 10s. $11\frac{1}{10}$d.
   (5) £2 0s. $4\frac{1}{2}$d.
   (6) $8\frac{3}{4}$ yd.
   (7) 1 oz. $2\frac{1}{2}$ dwt.
   (8) 30 sheep.
   (9) 21 acres 3 rd. 20 poles.
   (10) 2 bush.

3. (1) £1 13s. $7\frac{1}{2}$d.
   (2) £1 17s. $11\frac{1}{2}$d.
   (3) £1 15s. 4d.
   (4) 5s. 6d.
   (5) £32 15s. $6\frac{9}{10}$d.

4. (1) 12s.
   (2) £100 3s. 4d.
   (3) 4s. 2d.
   (4) 4d.
   (5) £2 14s. $3\frac{3}{5}$d.

5. (1) £15.
   (2) £31 10s.
   (3) £91 17s. $9\frac{3}{4}$d.
   (4) £57 10s. $10\frac{1}{3}$d.
   (5) £5 11s.

Exercise 38, page 143

1. 25.
2. $11\frac{1}{9}$.
3. 5.
4. $1\frac{1}{4}$.
5. 20.
6. 50.

7. 4.
8. 75.
9. 15.
10. $6\frac{2}{3}$.
11. 5.

12. $2\frac{1}{2}$.
13. $12\frac{1}{2}$.
14. 40.
15. $11\frac{1}{9}$.
16. 200

Exercise 39, page 145

1. 21·8%.
2. $52\frac{1}{12}$% of girls; $47\frac{11}{12}$% of boys.
3. 95% (actually $94\frac{73}{74}$).
4. 3·82.

5. £33 18s.
6. £1 6s.
7. £2 6s. 6d.
8. 84 lb., 16$\frac{4}{5}$ lb., 11$\frac{1}{5}$ lb.
9. First partner receives £333; second partner £270; third partner £207.
10. 43·68 lb. av. = 53·083 (3 repeating) lb. Troy.
11. 53%.
12. 63·19%.
13. 18$\frac{2}{11}$%.
14. £63 15s. 5$\frac{1}{4}$d.
15. 20·18%; 13·51%; 24·60%; 5·28%.
16. $\begin{cases} \text{Sum that must be insured} = £3\ 245\ 10s.\ 6d.\ (4\frac{11}{13}). \\ \text{Premium} \qquad\qquad\qquad = £153\ 10s.\ 6d. \end{cases}$
17. £48 3s. 9$\frac{9}{10}$d.
18. 13·84%.
19. 23·87%.

EXERCISE 40, page 153

1. 44 sq. yd.
2. 222 sq. ft.
3. 5$\frac{1}{4}$ sq. yd.
4. 4·698 acres.
5. 120$\frac{40}{63}$ yd., ∴ 121 yd.
6. 119 yd.
7. £5 16s. 8d.
8. £28 8s. 4d.
9. £34 0s. 2d.
10. 54 sq. ft.
11. 10s. 10$\frac{5}{24}$d.
12. 209$\frac{11}{21}$ yd., ∴ 210 yd.
13. £17 17s.
14. £50 8s.
15. (1) 115 yd.
    (2) 12s. 1d.
16. £379 13s.
17. (1) 56$\frac{4}{7}$ pieces, ∴ 57 *whole* pieces.
    (2) £102 12s.
18. £62 3s. 7$\frac{1}{2}$d.
19. (1) 60 000 francs.
    (2) £60 14s. 7d.
20. £182 8s.
21. 12 130 560 acres.
22. 1$\frac{5}{8}$ sq. ft.
23. 16s. 9d.

EXERCISE 41, page 159

1. 231 cu. ft.
2. 234 375 cu. ft.
3. 245 000 oz. = 6 tons 16 cwt. 2 qr. 24$\frac{1}{2}$ lb.
4. £630.
5. 33$\frac{1}{3}$ ft. (33·4 . . .).
6. 4 440 744 gall.
7. 1$\frac{3}{4}$ cu. ft. (theoretically more, if edges and corners are included).
8. $\frac{1}{864}$ in.
9. 34 yd. 2 ft. 2 in.
10. 19·7 in.
11. 108 tons 9 cwt. 72 lb.
12. 40 tons 11 cwt. 105$\frac{1}{2}$ lb.

EXERCISE 42, page 165

1. 437 sq. yd.; 16·58 yd.
2. 237½ sq. ft. approx.

3. 23 120 cu. yd.

4. 524·2 sq. yd.; 108·3 yd. (If E is a point due south of A and due east of D, AED is a right-angled triangle with two *equal* sides. Thus AE (= ED) can be found by Pythagoras' Theorem.)

5. 706·86 sq. yd.
6. 293¾ yd. (nearly).
7. 19·92 cu. in.
8. 250·12 lb.

9. 126·6 lb.
10. 12 937½ cu. ft.
11. 219½ sq. in. (nearly).
12. Almost 26 cu. in.

EXERCISE 43, page 171

1. £46 15s.
2. (1) £7 8s. 5d. (to nearest penny).
   (2) £44 10s. 5d. (to nearest penny).
3. £220 1s.
4. £19 11s. 9d. (nearly).
5. £325 8s. 9d. (nearly).
6. £60 16s.
7. £6 14s. ($\frac{156}{1825}$).
11. 4½ years.
12. £750.
13. 4½%.
14. £1 133 2s. 10d.

8. (1) £17 6s. 5d. (nearly).
   (2) £2 927 13s. 4d.
9. £8 10s. 10½d. (0·48 . . .).
10. £ 133 17s. 9d. ($9\frac{117}{365}$).
   (2) £2 024 7s. 9d.
15. 2½% (nearly).
16. 25%.
17. £291 13s. 4d.

EXERCISE 44, page 176

1. £20 4s.
2. £48 1s. 0d. (11·6d.) (nearly).
3. £43 14s. 3d. (nearly).
4. £34 8s. 5d. (nearly).
5. £325 5s. 4d.
6. £422 6s. 1d. (to nearest penny).
7. £298 6s. 2d.
8. £1 350 17s. 6d.

9. £118.
10. (1) £325 5s. 4d. (nearly).
   (2) £30 0s. 6d. (nearly).
11. £352 13s.
12. £268 4s. 6d.
13. £356 18s. 2d.
14. (a) £686 7s. 6d.
   (b) £919 16s. 2d.

EXERCISE 45, page 179

1. 20%.
2. £1 5s. 10d. per 100.
3. 12½%.
4. 4s. 7½d. (4s. 7⅓).

5. £3 6s. 6$\frac{6}{25}$d. gain.
6. 28.3%.
7. 11·76%.
8. 15%; 20%; 18¾%.